99

Lessons Learned From Disney

to Improve The Patient Experience

by

Jake Poore

President & Chief Experience Officer
Integrated Loyalty Systems, Inc.

Integrated Loyalty Systems
Elevating the Human Side of Healthcare

Testimonials

"Several years ago, I was the cynic in the strategy meeting, saying "This too will pass, just like every other corporate initiative..." Little did I realize that THIS is the stuff that makes the patient experience come to life within an organization. Jake has a way with creating an awe-inspiring, best-in-class experience. Simple, but not always easy... And when I had the opportunity to change and build a culture within my own organization, Jake was the first person I called. He has not only demonstrated the tools and experience necessary to deliver an exceptional patient experience, but has artfully helped change and create an amazing culture within my organization. I had both the opportunity to see the work come to life and then unequivocally hired Jake and his team to help me design our culture and make it patient-driven. One of the best decisions I ever made!"

— **Joseph Jasser,** MD, MBA, Former President/CEO
Dignity Health Medical Foundation

"This clear and intentional book is an invaluable tool for those healthcare leaders committed to making a difference and leading a culture revolution. Jake Poore loves the work he does and the teams that he works with, and this comes through in this terrific collection of practical tactics and reminders that will equip those ready to lead with an invaluable resource. If used well these pages will become dog-eared, well thumbed and widely shared. Thank you Jake for your leadership and for sharing your passion – we are all better for it."

— **Richard Corder**, Partner, Wellesley Partners
Culture Shepherd and Chief Experience Officer

"Jake Poore's book, *99 Lessons Learned From Disney to Improve the Patient Experience*, is a wonderful resource for any health care organization that desires to improve the patient experience. As a former member of the Disney team myself, I can confidently state that Jake has truly captured the essence of Disney's principles for creating loyalty-driving experiences. And more importantly, he has thoughtfully and artfully applied these principles to the world of health care. For 17 years, Jake and his team at ILS have been helping health care organizations successfully apply the lessons contained in this book. The lessons are field-tested and they work. I highly recommend this book!"

— **Dennis Snow**, President, Snow & Associates, Inc.
Author of *Unleashing Excellence: the Complete Guide to Ultimate Customer Service*

"It has been my honor and privilege to know Jake Poore as a business partner, colleague, collaborator and friend for the last 20 years. His speeches, workshops and engagements have distinguished him in elevating the human side of healthcare. Above all, Jake is an incomparable storyteller. I've often thought that his stories could stand alone as a field guide for healthcare professionals. We are all fortunate that he has finally written this book. It is a compilation of every story I've heard him tell... and then some. If you've been lucky enough to hear him speak, this book will serve as a perfect refresher course, reminding you of why we chose a profession in healthcare in the first place. If you haven't had the good fortune to hear him, this book will give you an introduction through captivating and compelling stories which forcefully illustrate what is possible when we follow his lead... and what's at stake if we don't. I highly recommend **99 Lessons Learned From Disney to Improve the Patient Experience** to everyone who works in healthcare."

— **Brian Wong**, MD, MPH, CEO, The Bedside Trust

"Jake Poore has distinguished himself as a leader in driving patient care improvements around the world. I have had the privilege of working with Jake and his team over the past two decades—with extraordinary results at both the University of Chicago Medical Center and the University of Pennsylvania Health System. His innovative, yet practical, solutions for placing patients and their families at the center of our work is an inspiration to us all. "99 Lessons" is a must read for all who continue to dedicate themselves to making a difference each and every day in the lives of our patients and their families."

— **Judy L. Schueler,** Vice President (retired),
University of Pennsylvania Health System

"I have firsthand knowledge of Jake's deep knowledge and understanding of the healthcare service industry and particularly how outstanding service can transform healthcare organizations to provide unusually high cost-effective quality at a time of diminishing reimbursement. Jake is my 'go to' person for all issues pertaining to healthcare service quality and I am proud that he is a member of my consulting network and represents the best of what the industry has to offer."

— **Jon Burroughs**, MD, MBA, FACHE, FAAPL,
President and CEO
The Burroughs Healthcare Consulting Network, Inc.

Copyright © 2019 by Integrated Loyalty Systems

Published by Integrated Loyalty Systems

First Printing: March 2019

Library of Congress Catalog Number: on file
       Poore, Jake

99 Lessons Learned From Disney to Improve the Patient Experience

ISBN: 978-0-9983434-0-2

Cover design and composition by Jonathan Pennell

First Integrated Loyalty Systems Edition
10   9 8 7 6   5 4   3 2 1
Printed in the United States of America

Dedication

To my friends and colleagues whom I was lucky enough to work with at Disney, thank you for the cherished magical memories and lifelong friendships. I learned something from each one of you and I am forever honored to have worked alongside you ~ making it *the happiest place on earth.*

To the care team members, healthcare leaders, and patients I am privileged to work with as partners in improving the patient experience; thank you for your stories, dedication, and passion. You inspire me every day.

To my team members at our company, Integrated Loyalty Systems (ILS), who have helped me spread the word and change the world, one doctor, one hospital, one patient at a time; thank you for your hard work and dedication to embracing our shared vision and for joining me on this incredible journey.

To my mother, Barbara, a nurse who always found ways to make healthcare a better place for healing and a better place to work, I hope I am making you proud, Mom. To my father, Eddie Allen, and my grandmother, Fannie Farrell, who both inspired me to go into healthcare and encouraged me to always follow my passion. To my sister, Kelli Hawkins, who became a nurse to follow her calling to care for others. To my sister, Karla, who was born with Down syndrome and medical complications so severe she wasn't supposed to live past the age of two (she is now in her 60s); thank you for keeping me humble and grounded. And to my brothers Rick and Terry, and my dad, thank you for your proud service in the U.S. armed forces.

To my children, Alayna, Logan, and Brielle, who put up with Daddy's relentless travel schedule. You are the reason I do what I do and while I am passionate about my work, nothing beats coming home to you.

I feel like I'm the luckiest guy in the world to do the work I do every day. But my work, and this book in particular, would still be just a dream if not for the fierce dedication of one person — my wife, Jenna.

Jenna has been with me since the very beginning, when we first launched this business together more than 17 years ago in a makeshift office in our garage (just like Walt and Roy Disney). In those early days she worked triple duty at a full-time day job; she functioned as a single parent to our three children while I was on the road working with clients; and she managed our business every night and weekend. Her belief in me and in this company, from day one, has been unwavering.

Jenna is more than just my trusted business partner; she's my life partner and the mother to our three children, and for that I am forever grateful. Thank you for everything.

Contents

Leadership

Employee Best Practices

Understand the Customer's Perspective: "Through the Patient's Eyes"

Service Behaviors

Create a Caring Language

Human Kindness at Work

Everything Speaks (Physical Environment)

Culture

Appendices

My Story

My father had a heart attack while on a fishing trip with friends in Michigan.

He was rushed to the local emergency department and immediately admitted to the Cardiac Care Unit. He needed extensive heart surgery to help save his life. After conducting some research, I was relieved to find out that this **hospital specialized in heart surgeries and had excellent clinical outcomes.**

I took the first possible flight from my home in Orlando to be with him prior to his surgery. When I arrived, he was in good spirits and was even joking with the nurses and doctors caring for him. Everyone politely called my dad, "Mr. Poore," but he gently corrected each one of them by saying, *"Please, just call me, Eddie, everyone does."* They would always reply, *"Okay, Eddie. And I'll make sure everyone else on the team knows that, too."* Every new employee who entered his room, however, would immediately address him as "Hello, Mr. Poore." My dad continued to reply, *"Please, just call me, Eddie,"* but they never seemed to get it right. After a while, Dad became understandably frustrated and concerned about his care team's inability to communicate his name effectively. Later that night, when a new nurse was about to hang a new IV bag for my dad and was in the process of adding drugs to it, I asked her what was she giving my dad. She told me it was medicine to thin his blood (I made a mental note).

Every new employee who came in the room would notice my dad's gold necklaces, and would say, "I see you have some jewelry around your neck. Since you're going into surgery, you'll need to take them off." They offered to take them off right then and send them to security for safe keeping. These necklaces had sentimental value to my father: one was from his mother who died shortly after giving birth to my dad, and the other was from his deceased wife. He made it clear that he didn't want them removed! He would get upset and say he needed them, reiterating that they had great sentimental value and he wanted them to stay on his body, even during surgery. One nurse finally agreed that the necklaces would be taped to one of his legs during the surgery so that he'd always have them on him. *Unfortunately, this too, was never communicated to the surgical staff.*

Every time someone new walked into his room, they would constantly call him, "Mister Poore" and kindly offer "to take off those gold necklaces." Finally, my dad lost his temper. I remember watching his vital signs spike on the monitor above his bed: it appeared that his blood pressure, pulse, and respiration all would rise… clearly, there were clinical implications to this poor team communication. **To my dad, the two most important things to him were his good name and his gold necklaces, yet they couldn't seem to get either of these right.**

Later, I was invited to escort my dad as they wheeled him down to surgery. As I was about to say goodbye to my dad and wish him well, a surgical employee addressed my father, "Hi, Mr. Poore (not "Eddie"), I'm the nurse anesthetist. Do you know what that means?" My father replied, "Yes, you're going to put me to sleep, I guess." And she continued, "Yep, that's right. And I see you have some gold necklaces on, let's…." While she was still speaking, my father turned to me with a huge look of fear on his face and said, "Good Lord! If they can't even get these necklaces right….!" That was pretty much the last thing he said on this earth.

An important side note: While in the surgical waiting room, I picked up a newspaper and read that President Bill Clinton had been scheduled to have his heart surgery that same week, but his doctors wanted him to wait a few extra days until all the blood thinner had left his body. This reminded me of the nurse who had administered blood thinners into my dad's IV only the night before.

After my fathers' surgery, the surgeon didn't come out to talk to me, which I worried was a bad sign. Instead, he sent out someone in scrubs to inform us of what had happened.

My father died on the operating table that day.

When I asked for the cause of death, she explained, "Your father couldn't hold his sutures. He just bled out."

I asked if the blood thinner he was given the night before had anything to do with that. She immediately replied, "Blood thinner? What blood thinner?"

In shock and complete disbelief, I found myself recalling the complete inability to communicate displayed by my dad's medical team since the moment I had arrived. His team couldn't communicate *the name* he wanted to be called or remember about his gold necklaces. I wondered if they failed to communicate the blood thinner too.

I find that most patients and visitors are experts at what they know and understand, and they will judge you on what they *don't know and don't understand.* Here's what we *did* know and understand: My dad's medical team couldn't get his name right, and nobody communicated the plan for his gold necklaces. As non-clinical family members, it made sense to us that the inability to get those two things right was directly tied to the inability to get the clinical part of my dad's care right.

Obviously, the loss of my father is an extremely personal and painful memory. I share it with you because I firmly believe that it doesn't have to be this way. My dad's story, and the realization that the same mistake can be made again, is at the heart of what fuels me and keeps me up at night.

My dad's story is about more than just a bad technical or clinical outcome. It's also about the *human side* of his experience. The communication between the doctors and nurses on the care team was severely lacking and the communication between my father and his care team was even worse.

To his doctors and nurses, he was just the '4:00 PM' valve replacement, or the 'double bypass in OR2.'

But to me, he was Eddie Poore. He was my hero, and he was my dad. And now he is the reason why I am on a mission to change the face of healthcare. I believe that there are things that we can do every day in healthcare that will make it better. And that if they'd been done at this hospital, my dad might not have died. I want to help avoid situations like these from ever happening again. It is my personal mission.

Eddie Poore

Thank you for joining me on this journey!

Introduction

How would **you** best describe the magic of the Disney? Would you talk about the amazing attractions, entertaining live shows, or the beautiful resorts? Or maybe it's the world renowned friendly and knowledgable cast members and their ability to anticipate your every need? Or perhaps the universal appeal of Mickey Mouse and the rest of the Disney characters? Is it Disney's fanatic attention to detail, its ability to keep the place so clean, and the dedication to entertain you even while you wait that sets Disney apart as the gold standard in entertainment? While each of these things definitely contributes to the magic of Disney, they're all just pieces to a larger puzzle. A puzzle of interlocking pieces held together with a culture of consistency.

But what's the common glue that holds all those pieces together? That's what I would like to explore with you in this book: both the many pieces that make up this mosaic called *The Disney Experience,* and also the glue that helps fuse it all together. Can any of these elements be adapted, adopted, or literally transplanted into the world of healthcare?

Creating Memorable Experiences

When I think about creating memorable experiences, I can't help but recall the nearly two decades I spent working at The Walt Disney Company, where I was lucky enough to hold many unique jobs. My first job was with the Disney College Program as an hourly cast member selling balloons on Main Street U.S.A. in the Magic Kingdom. Years later, I

became a leader and helped launch many ne
including the Disney Vacation Club and the woi
Disney Institute.

But no matter how different and challenging each job i
my role in the show was always crystal clear an
changed. The glue that holds the entire Disney cast togi
our focus on the same goal or service theme: We create hap
by providing the finest in entertainment for people of all
everywhere.

At the Walt Disney World Resort, all 74,000+ cast members (c
employees) are all helping to tell a common story because we are
all aligned toward one shared goal: "We Create Happiness." That's
why everything seems so magical ... because it is! Even though
every cast member has a different job title, tasks, and
responsibilities, everyone knows that their *role in the show* is to
create happiness.

> *The Magic Kingdom custodial cast member sweeps the street;*
> *but also creates happiness by also helping guests discover the*
> *very best spot to watch the parade and fireworks show.*

> *The ice cream server scoops ice cream all day, but also*
> *creates happiness by immediately replacing a child's spilled*
> *cone as soon as it hits the ground, before one tear is shed.*

> *Snow White gives autographs and takes photos with guests all*
> *day, but she also creates happiness by communicating in sign*
> *language with a hearing-impaired guest.*

> *A security officer conducts safety checks on people and their*
> *bags all day long at the theme park main entrance, but he*
> *also creates happiness when he abruptly stops, bows at the*
> *waist, and announces, "Oh, good morning, your highness!", in*

honor of a four year old little girl who arrives wearing a Cinderella dress, glass slippers, and tiara on her head.

The Heart of the Disney Difference

The art of delivering consistently exceptional customer service IS at the heart of the Disney Difference. Service can't just be something that you do, it has to become *who you are* as an organization. It must be woven into your organizational DNA. It's something I believe can also be harnessed and replicated in healthcare.

Alignment: Everyone Must Be Pointed In The Same Direction

The first step on your journey to excellence is to get everyone aligned toward a common goal or purpose. We call this your organizational **True North**.

I used to tell new Disney cast members in new employee orientation, called Disney Traditions, "Our Disney Service Theme is like a light at the end of a tunnel that everyone heads toward. We may never reach that light, but it guides every step of our journey and helps us all focus on the same destination." When you have alignment, you get concerted effort. Interestingly, the root word of "concerted" is concert. Very much like an orchestra playing a concert, even though everyone plays different notes on different instruments, together they play beautiful music. The same is true for us when we are all on the same page, focused in the same direction.

At Disney, we created alignment by getting everyone focused on the first three words of the Walt Disney World Service Theme: *We Create Happiness...*

Similarly, at Dignity Health Medical Foundation, my training and consulting firm helped build alignment of 3,500 employees and providers across the entire state of California by getting everyone focused on the first five words of *their* Organizational True North: *We Unite Healing and HumanKindness.*

Your Service Theme or True North will be different because your organization is unique. And while it may seem impossible at first, success will come when you begin with the key leaders within your organization (formal and informal), encouraging them to get involved in the process of designing the blueprints for your new organizational culture. This will allow the first wave of change-makers to clearly articulate what your company will and will not stand for moving forward.

Our experience has shown us that employees and physicians are much more likely to own the cultural design process when they are given an opportunity to participate in it. After building cultures and the scaffolding that supports it for more than 20 years, I have found that *authorship leads to ownership.* And *ownership leads to pride.* Pride motivates people to develop the courage to help protect what they have created…which leads to a wonderful thing called *mutual accountability.* When everyone is working towards a common purpose, using common tools, and speaking a common language, they've achieved concerted effort.

The music you play is really the experience you create. At this point, your job as a leader is to find and gather your organization's stories and share them daily with the rest of the organization. These stories become the flesh and blood of your organizational DNA, and this DNA is the reason your employees come to work every morning. It is also the reason local physicians will refer their patients to your organization, or not, and the reason patients seek you out as the destination of choice, or not. Ultimately, the DNA of your organization will become the reason you choose to stay with your employer, or not.

What kind of experience do you want to create for your patients and your employees? What do you want them to see, hear, and remember? **What do you want them to feel?**

It's Time to Think Differently

Albert Einstein once said, *The definition of insanity is doing the same thing over and over again and expecting different results.* Similarly, my father, Eddie Poore, would often say: *If you always do what you always did, you'll always get what you always got.* Or as my wise grandmother, Fannie Farrell, used to say: *If you always think the way you always thought, you will always do what you always did.*

So, don't we need to start thinking differently if we expect to start acting differently? Otherwise, aren't we just choosing t*he insanity defense?*

We have to think differently in healthcare, or we, too, will always do what we have always done.

Think about it. For more than 200 years we have continued to use terms that our customers still don't fully comprehend. For instance, we still use the term "discharge" when informing patients they are going home. I will never forget the look on my grandmother's face when the eye surgeon came into her hospital room, examined her eyes, and then said, "Congratulations, Mrs Farrell! Tomorrow we're gonna let you discharge!" She got confused and looked very uncomfortable. To an 87 year-old female who has not been in the hospital in over 30 years, the term "discharge" does not mean "go home." It means something totally different that can be uncomfortable and very personal.

Beyond the words that we use, we also have to start seeing the patient experience differently, or more holistically.

At your hospital or care facility, I'll bet there are hundreds of individual job titles and tasks that are focused on delivering on the *operational or clinical side* of the patient experience. But what about the service side? When it comes to creating truly exceptional patient experiences, you have to do more than just tell your employees, nurses, and doctors to "be nicer." You have to take into account the 4P's of the entire experience: the people, processes, product, and physical environment. Each of these aspects color how patients see, hear, touch, taste, and feel about your organization.

I think we can all agree that making the patient experience better is the right thing to do. But with the growing number of reimbursement dollars tied to patient satisfaction scores, it has also become a matter of financial survival.

Build a Culture with Intention

To really move the needle on patient experience, you need to begin with the end in mind. In other words, you need to create an *intentional culture.* If you do not create a culture with intention, then you have a culture by default. Every organization has a culture. The question becomes, can you articulate what that culture is and leverage it to align with your strategic plan? If your desire is to create a world-class organization where every employee is aligned to the goal of delivering exceptional service, where every employee can honestly say "this is the way we do things here," then you must become *intentional* in everything you do and say. This book is designed to help you get started.

I hope this book will be your catalyst to creating positive change within your organization.

How to Use This Book

I've been working with healthcare leaders like you for more than 20 years and there are a few things I know for sure:

You're passionate. You're driven. You're committed. And for most of you, your work is a calling, not just another job.

You want to improve the experience for your patients (and your employees, for that matter), but you're not quite sure where to start.

You don't have any extra time in your day!

Inside this book, you'll discover 99 gems, lessons, tips, and techniques I learned from both working at Disney and in healthcare. These lessons can be a great conversation starter with your team as you begin to improve and eventually transform your patient experience and employee engagement.

Think of these 99 lessons as individual logs around a campfire. Each one can ignite a spark in your employees. The sparks can fuel a greater bonfire that leads to employee interest, engagement, commitment, and ownership.

The beauty of this book is that you can pick it up whenever you need a dose of inspiration. Use it to kick-off team meetings, employee huddles, or during your leader or executive rounding. You can even use an idea and share it in a weekly email or employee newsletter.

If you have any of your own gems, tips, techniques, or photos you'd like to share, send them to us and we will share them with other difference makers.

Drop me a line at 99Lessons@WeCreateLoyalty.com or tweet me @jakepoore on Twitter. I'd love to hear from you.

Service Excellence

"Common sense becomes common practice

when the heart, head, and hands

are all engaged, aligned, and connected."

- Jake Poore

1

Connect Every Employee to a Purpose

My mantra for the fast growing workforce of the millennial generation is "if they don't know the **why**, the **what** doesn't matter." Perhaps the most important thing I learned in my 18+ years at Disney is you must connect people to a common purpose before you can teach them to be experts at their individual job tasks.   When you have a group of people, all singularly focused and aligned, you can then create consistency and continuity, and *that* helps create the "magic." If you don't, you unknowingly create a culture of silos, fiefdoms, and islands - where everyone is out for themselves and doing their own thing.

Employees need a clear 'end in mind' statement that becomes even greater than the sum of the statement's individual steps or parts. This statement must be short, memorable, and relevant to all. It should be something that is customer-driven and that every employee can equally contribute to making a reality. We know that every role is vital to the overall success. For the Walt Disney World Resort, that clear end in mind statement is called the Disney Service Theme, and the first three words are what all cast members remember: *"**We create happiness** by providing the finest in entertainment for people of all ages, everywhere."*

Because Disney is guest-driven, they consistently ask their loyal guests why they intend to return year after year. The guests say their top three reasons are:

1. The place is clean,

2. The employees are friendly, and

3. They had fun.

Clean, friendly, and fun. Always those three, always in that order.

So, how do you get 74,000 cast members to pick up trash? Well, you can't just say, "Do this or you're out of here." Instead, you tell them that picking up trash and keeping the place clean is the number one key driver to guest loyalty, and if we do this they will come back. So, at Disney, no one really wants to pick up trash, but everyone wants to help create happiness!

Everyone has a *role* in the show

A Disney theme park is very much like a Broadway show, where every member of the cast has an important contribution to make, or a role in the show. And any one cast member can impact whether that show becomes a world-class presentation or a world-class flop.

This concept also applies directly to healthcare. By following patients through their continuum of care, we know that they experience us horizontally (across departments), not vertically (within one department). Even within one department, doctors and care givers know they have a direct role in creating the ideal patient experience. They literally lay hands on the patients and help save lives. And when patients leave the hospital, they give hugs to those who cared for them.

But what about the rest of the employees? Ownership must also apply to the non-clinical healthcare employees, including food service, housekeeping, transporters, security, billing, valet parking, gift shop, and volunteers.

When everyone at Disney is focused on creating the ideal guest experience, it helps break down organizational silos, fiefdoms, and islands. Disney leaders help their cast members by reminding them of this saying:

> "If you're not taking care of the guest, you should be taking care of someone who is. Everyone has a role in the show."

Healthcare leaders can adapt this Disney mantra as well:

> "If you're not taking care of the patient, you should be taking care of someone who is. Everyone has a role on the care team."

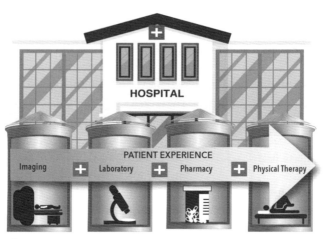

Patients experience healthcare horizontally, not vertically.

I believe the greatest challenge in healthcare is lack of employee purpose alignment. We, too, need to connect every employee to their role on the care team, not just to their daily job tasks. When sharing this important concept with one of our clients, Mercy Medical Group, a division of Dignity Health, we helped them develop employee alignment by creating this True North statement, "We Unite Healing and HumanKindness to create peace of mind for every person, every time, through a culture of yes."

And again, most care team members will probably only remember the first five words…and that's okay because, they created it!

Summed up best by one of their chief surgeons, Eric Morse, MD, "The best part of this True North statement is that it was created by us and our patients, for us and our patients." Can you hear the pride and the ownership in his voice?

We find that the closer you are to the patient in the experience, the easier it is to connect people to purpose. The further away you are from the patient's bedside, the harder it is for you to see your individual contributions to the care team. So can you also connect the back office employees to the care experience (positions like accounting, medical records, sterile processing, and engineering) so they can see how their specific role impacts the patient experience? I believe you can by creating a clear end-in-mind statement that synthesizes your mission, vision, and values, and by making sure it is patient-driven. Remember, the most powerful word in the statement is *WE!*

2

Create an Intentional Language of Service

Every organization has a culture, and it's either a culture with intention or a culture by default. To create an intentional culture or business experience, you must first create an intentional language that equips employees with the knowledge to be in sync with each other.

I've spent decades analyzing organizations that have successfully achieved the status of world-class, and I've discovered that world-class companies have many things in common. First, they all use clearly intentional words and phrases that help unite their employees to a *common language of service* that clearly symbolizes what the company will and will not stand for.

I first learned this when I began working at the Walt Disney World Resort in Orlando in 1982. At Disney, you learn the company's unique story quickly, and then seek to tell that story in everything you do and say by using unique words in everyday vernacular.

And at Disney, it all starts even before you're hired!

Disney's Language of Service

From the moment you apply for a job, you can tell Disney is in show business. They don't have a central employment office; they have the Disney *Casting Center*. And you don't interview for a job; *you audition for a role in the show*.

All roles are either *Onstage or Backstage* ... and every role is vital to a successful production. (What about your onstage and backstage areas? At National Rehabilitation Hospital in Washington D.C., they call their onstage areas Service Areas; there are no departments or clinics.)

At Disney, you don't wear a uniform. Everyone wears a *Costume* (whether they wear their own clothes or if a costume is given to them). Disney doesn't have customers; Disney welcomes and treats everyone as a *Guest*.

When Disney builds anything new (a hotel, attraction, or water park), they design and write out the ideal story for that product or experience. That story paints a picture of onstage, with cast members, and backstage, with a support team. A script is written and cast member auditions begin. Everything cast members do or say that adds value to the ideal story is called *Good Show*. Anything that detracts, distracts, or defaces the ideal experience is called *Bad Show*.

Disney doesn't have employees; they have *Cast Members*. Referring to employees as cast members is an intentional reminder that they're more than just their individual job title or function - everyone is a contributor, everyone matters, and every role is vital to the ideal show. It's a constant reminder that everyone has a specific role in the show and that show is to create happiness, not just to provide a bunch of rides, food, or beverages.

Every cast member knows that whether they wait tables, drive the monorail, or work in accounting, they all have a role in the show. And as cast members, they all have the same shared goal of creating happiness for "people of all ages, everywhere," including when those people are other cast members.

What Do You Call Your Employees?

The words you choose to call your employees can instill a sense of pride in your team and sends a message to your patients of everyone's role in the healing process. What words do you use to describe your employees as a whole? Are they your staff or your associates? I know it's spelled differently, but isn't "staph" an infection? Target stores call their employees associates. But you're not in the entertainment or retail business, you're in the healing business. So why wouldn't you call employees caregivers?

At Mercy Medical Group in California, they call every one of their employees Care Team Members, whether they work directly with patients or not.

In healthcare, we're not as explicit and as basic with changing our words as Disney. At the patient's first encounter with us, we tell them we're going to "triage" them. But patients have no idea what the word triage means. At their last onsite encounter with us, we tell patients they can "discharge." We've inherited 200 years of language that isn't always current or appropriate for patients today, nor is it patient-friendly. Unfortunately, many of us use it because *we've always done it that way*.

> **To Change Your Culture, You Must First Change Your Stories.**
>
> **To Change Your Stories, You Must First Change Your Words.**

If you want to change your culture, you must first change your stories. If you want to change your stories, you must first change your words to be more guest- or patient-centric.

A key in this cultural transformation process is not just what you create, it's how you get there. Try to avoid the pitfalls of imposing a script on your employees. Give them an opportunity to help you build it, verify what they create with patients, and hardwire it into your recruiting, onboarding, on the job training, and annual performance evaluations.

As leaders, it's our job to make the invisible, visible; the implicit, explicit. In business and in healthcare, we must be explicit about both favorable and forbidden phrases, and we can do that by getting back to the basics. Better still, to paraphrase the great Vince Lombardi, we need to become brilliant on the basics.

Words have power. If you want to create an intentional culture around service, you must first create an intentional language that fits that culture.

From day one as a Disney cast member, I learned many favorable phrases that can help build immediate rapport and trust and reinforce the ideal Disney story or experience. I also learned the forbidden phrases we should never use because they can break down rapport, erode trust, and even create unintended resentment. What language do you allow in your hospitals and organizations between physicians and nurses or other departments? How about between clinical and non-clinical employees? Consider the dangers of allowing these forbidden phrases to go unnoticed or unresolved. What might the unintended consequences be?

Having an intentional language of service sets employees up for success to deliver on their service promise by arming them with the tools they need to build the ideal show or experience. It also teaches them the things they must avoid so as to not distract from the ideal experience.

At my company, Integrated Loyalty Systems, we call unfavorable phrases *Verbal Graffiti*. We've helped many teams develop a list of favorable and forbidden phrases. Here are some examples:

Forbidden Phrases (Verbal Graffiti)

- Healthcare Jargon: mammo, discharge, triage
- Healthcare Acronyms: ER, IV, NPO, NICU, PICU, SOB
- We're short-staffed today."
- "I don't know," or "It's not my job."
- "Hey you!"
- "She is the hip replacement in 103."
- "I'm not on the clock yet," (or) "I'm off the clock now.
- "No." (and leaving it at that with no further explanation)
- "Next!"
- Using slang terms of endearment ("Hello honey, sweetie, dear, sugar, chief, dude....")
- And profanity of any kind

Favorable Phrases

- "I don't know, but I'll find out for you."
- "Let me take you there," or "Let me show you."
- "I understand."
- "It would be my pleasure to help you."
- "I'll be happy to take care of you."
- "Thank you for choosing us...."

Some of the best opportunities for identifying favorable phrases happens when you're doing a technique we call *Caring Out Loud*®, or narrating care.

> *"Let me close this curtain/door for your privacy."*

For example:

> "For your privacy, let me invite your family members to step out of the room while you undress."

> "To be sure we are being as personable as possible, we want to call you by the name you like best. What name shall we call you while you're with us?"

The first step on your journey to creating a formal language of caring is to pay attention to everyone you interact with in your community. Wherever you shop, service your car, worship, vacation, or travel, start collecting favorable phrases that make you smile and forbidden phrases that make you mad. For example, when I go through a Chick-Fil-A restaurant drive-thru, and they hand me my meal, I normally say, "Thank you." They always reply, "It's my pleasure." And I always smile! They do this task always… every time…at every location. This little thing has become a hallmark for that fast food restaurant. It first starts with simplicity and consistency and then, over time, sincerity and authenticity will follow.

Most employees will do the right thing, but sometimes they just don't know how. When you leave it up to them to figure it out on their own, you roll the dice. However, you and your team can easily sit down and write out the story of the ideal patient experience in your department (and verify it with your patient and family advisory council). Then, start to identify words and phrases that add value and build trust, as well as those that unintentionally add anxiety or stress, remove value, and erode trust.

3

Wear Your Name Tag
Over Your Heart

When did employees start wearing name tags? What was their original purpose? Most would say to let the customer know that this person officially works here. A second reason would be to make a connection or bond with those they serve. The name tag should speak for itself, "Hi, my name is Jacklyn, I work here and I'm here to help!"

But why do patients and visitors tell us that employee name tags are such a frustration in healthcare today? First, because they can't read them! Most are identification badges clipped to a necklace lanyard, not actual name tags. They are often found dangling, flipped over, or even laying on the wearer's lap for those employees who sit at their desks. They serve so many internal purposes: security, clocking in/out, opening automatic doors on secure floors, even buying food in the cafeteria. But what was their original purpose? I believe it was to build a connection with those you care for.

When we first begin a client engagement, our team conducts a "Pride Audit" (mystery shopping) as part of our initial cultural assessment. Out of the thousands of employee name tags we have observed at hundreds of hospitals and facilities over the last 15 years, more than 50 percent of them were flipped over — no surprise given that most name tags are on a lanyard or pull-string. It's hard to connect with someone when you can't even read their name tag.

Another concern patients voice is that they don't know what you do based on all the acronyms on your ID badge. Most patients did not go to medical school or nursing school and do not carry a healthcare acronym glossary around with them. Of course, name tags would not be necessary in business if everyone introduced themselves and their role, but since healthcare is heavily regulated, identification badges aren't going away anytime soon. Given the fact that an average patient will interact with many employees during a hospital stay, each interaction the patient has with team members either contributes to building bonds or eroding them.

The Ideal Name Tag

Perhaps the best example of the ideal name tag is the one you see on cast members at the Walt Disney Company. Every one of their 100,000+ Disney cast members worldwide has an oval-shaped name tag. Cast Member name tags display both their first name and their home town (city, state, or country), and it serves to help make a connection with those they interact with every day.

The first marker of a Disney cast member's name tag is that the name is printed in a clearly legible, large font - nothing fancy to distract or confuse.

Next, it includes a company logo like Mickey Mouse or Cinderella Castle, which always makes people smile. And to further improve guest service, cast members can earn up to five other language symbols attached to their name tag, making it easy for a guest to know who speaks their language.

And last, the name tag serves as a connector or bridge-maker. Guests who visit Disney come from all around the world. Imagine how easily a connection can be made when you see a cast member from your hometown or a place you've always wanted to visit? It's a great conversation starter. Also, the Disney name tag is worn on the employee's left side, over the heart, as a symbolic reminder to show care and compassion to each guest.

4

Maintain an Onstage Mentality

The Walt Disney Company is masterful at designing and producing quality shows that are consistent day in and day out, year after year. One of the ways they're able to maintain an exceptional show is by clearly identifying what is acceptable onstage and what should be taken backstage, or offstage. This concept goes beyond parades and shows. It applies to every department and every aspect of the business.

When visiting a Disney theme park, you would never see a garbage collection truck driving down Main Street U.S.A.. Similarly, you'll never see an employee eating, drinking, smoking, talking on their cell phone, or using foul language while onstage. Of course, Disney cast members may have to do those things, but they do them backstage. Disney would say anything that distracts or detracts from the ideal show is **bad show.** Likewise, the things they do consistently that add value to the show is what they call **good show.**

Onstage and Backstage in Healthcare

Because we haven't clearly delineated what is onstage and backstage in healthcare and what would be considered good show and bad show, we unintentionally blur the lines and bring our backstage dirty laundry onstage.

In a healthcare setting, patients don't want to hear medical personnel talking about how short-staffed they are or how tired they are. They don't want to see someone duct-taping a piece of medical equipment as a temporary fix. They don't want to see crusty old food on the cafeteria fork. They don't want to overhear everything that's going on in the hospital through someone's two-way radio hooked to their belt. All of this is considered bad show because it gives the impression that the facility is chaotic, in disarray, and unsafe.

Disney has signs on certain backstage doorways that say, "You are now stepping onstage." Consider placing a sign or even a mirror at the exit of employee break areas to remind your employees to switch to an **onstage mentality** and ensure they're ready to be onstage in patient areas.

5

Make Someone Smile by "Taking 5"

"Taking 5"

When I was a cast member and leader at Walt Disney World, we knew that between 25-35 million people would come to visit every year, and an average family would interact with between 60-70 cast members each day of their Disney vacation. And, if they came during a busy time of the year, they may wait a long time for each attraction. Some guests told us they felt like "a wallet with legs."

To help overcome this perception, Disney leaders encouraged us to strive to **Take 5** with one guest a day. Take 5 was a challenge to take five minutes with one family per day to make them feel special, make them smile, or just single them out.

Back in the late 1980s, my first job at Disney was selling balloons on Main Street at the Magic Kingdom. My trainer shared a great Take 5 technique that he would use to make people feel special. If someone walked by wearing a baseball cap, he'd call out the name of the team on the cap. For example, 'Oh, I love the Cubs!'

Those few simple words were a great conversation starter and led to more personalized service as he helped them find their favorite attraction, the nearest restroom, or the best location for the parade.

If more than one cast member took a Take 5 with the same family, that's when the family would start to say, *Hey, what do they put in the water around here? Everyone is so nice!* If many people do it, it becomes a hallmark for Disney. And it could become a hallmark for your hospital too.

Magic Moments

Because Disney strives to capture and tell stories, the best ideas shared around these Take 5 moments were ultimately transformed into what Disney calls "MAGIC MOMENTS." If Take 5s were random acts of kindness to make people feel special, Magic Moments were prepared and orchestrated Take 5 moments that had now been **operationalized.**

Sometimes magic happens when and where you least expect it. One such example of a Take 5 that turned into an orchestrated Magic Moment is the origami towels created by Disney housekeepers.

It all started with one housekeeper who took a towel and made it into a flower (a "Take 5"). The guests liked it so much that Disney leaders invited the housekeeper to teach others on her team how to fold a towel into a flower. At that point, it became more than just a random act of kindness from one employee - it become business as usual for the housekeeping team.

While resort guests are out enjoying the Disney theme parks, these *magic-maker* housekeepers use extra bath towels and washcloths to create unique towel origami shapes and animals. They might arrange your kid's stuffed animals so it looks like Mickey

and Minnie are watching TV, having a picnic, or even brushing their teeth with shower caps on. When guests return to their hotel room at the end of the day, they never know what kind of special surprise will be waiting to greet them.

So you see, housekeepers are not just cleaning rooms, they are also creating happiness.

Part of the legacy Walt Disney handed down to his leaders was for Disney managers to dress in plain clothes and stand in line and listen carefully to their guests. Guests are often overheard saying, "I can't wait to go back to my room to see what happened in our room...I wonder what the Disney fairy did today?"

Your housekeeping team can bring the same kind of magic to your patients too. Towel origami is easy to learn and the cost is nothing more than a few extra hand towels you already have on hand. Likewise, having fun with a child's stuffed animal, toy, or other small prop requires just a small investment of time and is a great way to bring smiles to young patients (and the young at heart!)

> *Housekeepers are not just cleaning rooms, they are creating happiness.*

6

Create Warm Welcomes

They say you never get a second chance to make a first impression. What is the first impression in your business, hospital, or clinic? Who is responsible for making the right first impressions? Are these first impressions warm and friendly, or cold and impersonal?

One of the best examples of a warm welcome I can think of is "Richard," the elderly gentleman who greeted guests at Disney's Grand Floridian Resort for many years. His job was to create a warm welcome for everyone entering the resort – and boy did he own it! He tipped his hat, held the door open, took photos with his adoring fans, and shared an infectious smile with everyone. People loved him!

If you're a member of the timeshare experience known as Disney Vacation Club, you know that the security guard at the entrance to the parking lot greets every guest with, "Welcome home!"

A receptionist at Mass Mutual Insurance Company in Springfield, Massachusetts has a name plate in front of her desk that says "Director of First Impressions."

> Director of First Impressions

In healthcare, our patients arrive nervous, scared, anxious, and unsure. A warm welcome can make them feel a little more at ease.

Whether it's a friendly word or greeting, a smile or handshake, holding the door open, or escorting the patient to the exam room, the best part of a warm welcome is that it doesn't cost any money and anyone can do it.

Anyone that comes in contact with patients, both medical and non-medical personnel, has the opportunity to create a warm welcome. One of the best ways to create a warm welcome with patients is to ask them the name they prefer to be called, record it for all on the care team to reference, and then use it **every time.**

Is valet parking part of your health system? What about your security team? Are they contracted through an outside company? Are they up-to-speed on how to deliver warm welcomes? They should be! This way, no matter where a patient or visitor arrives, warm welcomes are part of their experience.

7

Turn Handoffs Into Handovers

Healthcare is incredibly complex. It can be incredibly challenging to navigate from one department to another, even within a single hospital. Well-meaning employees love to give directions and tell people where to go; however, sometimes it's better to walk them there.

When we send someone to another department, we call that a handoff – just like in a relay race. To ensure handoffs are done in the best way possible, turn the hand<u>off</u> into a hand<u>over</u>.

At Disney, children often get separated from their family. When a cast member spots a lost child, they first walk the child around the immediate area to see if the parents are nearby. After that, the child is brought to Main Street City Hall so security can be notified. But instead of just dropping the child off and returning to their work area, the cast member creates a handover with the cast member working at City Hall.

Knowing the child is probably scared, the cast member introduces the child to the City Hall cast member and says, "Hi Jim, good to see you again. This is Logan. Logan lost his parents somewhere around Space Mountain. Logan, this is Jim. He's an expert at finding lost parents."

It's the proverbial joining of the hands. By connecting your customer, guest, or patient with the next person in the encounter, you reassure them that they're being well cared for.

Here's an example of what a handoff versus a handover might look like in healthcare:

HANDOFF

Doctor to his patient, Jenna: "Ok Jenna, just take the elevator down two floors to radiology. They'll take some pictures and call me when they're finished."

HANDOVER (involves walking patient to the imaging area)

Doctor to radiology technologist: "Hi John, this is my patient, Jenna. Jenna, John is going to take a series of x-rays, as you and I discussed. As soon as he's finished, he'll notify me…" The warm handover technique is also a great way to avoid the "out of sight, out of mind" mentality that can often occur when the patient is moved to another floor or to another department.

Handovers don't always happen in person. Think of the care team member that answers your phone. Instead of answering the phone and transferring patient Anna Duncan to Jim Smith in the billing office, your reception team member might say, "Mr. Smith, I have Miss Anna Duncan on the line. She needs to discuss her bill. Miss Duncan, it's my pleasure to connect you to Jim Smith who can help you with your questions."

8

Empower Your Team to Create Service Heroes

One of the best ways Disney creates world-class experiences is to arm their cast members with simple tools and training to help other cast members become service heroes.

Many times this is done by using the warm handover technique we discussed in the previous lesson. Everyone knows that a typical "handoff" sometimes results in the baton getting dropped, meaning the patient gets lost or a promise is left unfulfilled. But a *handover* is done with two hands, introducing the guest to the team member or calling the team member ahead of time and preparing them to delight the guest you're sending to them.

> *Handoffs are risky, but handovers are orchestrated.*

A great example of a terrific handover that set up the next team to be service heroes occurred at the University of Chicago Medicine, at the main entrance of the Duchossois Center for Advanced Medicine (DCAM). The security officer there, Sammy Hill (dressed like a hotel bellman), opens the car door and warmly greets the patient, Mrs. Margaret Jones, by saying, "Good morning, Betty, and welcome back! It's good to see you again." Betty is elated that he remembers her and says, "Oh Sammy, aren't you a sweetie! You're the only one who calls me Betty! I tell everyone to call me Betty, but here they either call me 'Margaret' or 'Mrs. Jones'. Bless *you* Sammy!"

Betty also mentions that today is "graduation day," marking her last oncology treatment for cancer. Armed with this important piece of information, Sammy calls upstairs to remind the oncology-hematology team that Mr. and Mrs. Jones are on their way up, that she loves to be called Betty, and that today is her GRADUATION DAY. When Mr. Jones pushes Betty's wheelchair off the elevator, the three people working at the oncology-hematology reception desk stand up and greet her with cheers!

Sammy successfully set up that reception team to be service heroes in the eyes of this patient! And how do you think that made Betty and her husband feel? How do you think it made Sammy and the reception team feel?

9

Create a Fond Farewell

As weary guests make their way to the exits of a Disney theme park late at night, they are often met by smiling cast members wearing gigantic four-finger Mickey Mouse gloves, waving goodbye and saying "goodnight, thank-you for visiting us today, safe travels home…and we'll see you real soon!" It's a nice touch at the end of a long day of having fun, and it's a nice way to send guests home with a fond farewell. Each night, department leads from various departments will schedule cast for this specific role. This is an orchestrated moment for the Disney experience.

In contrast, the last touchpoint of the patient experience is not considered a fond farewell. As matter of fact, it is called a discharge! Clearly, most healthcare experiences are not fun and can be very painful. But why can't we send them off with a fond farewell as well? Many times patients tell us we unintentionally overwhelm and overload them with information on the last hour of their hospital stay. Sometimes, we even make it difficult for their spouse or family member to find a temporary parking spot so they can quickly and efficiently pick up their loved one.

The place we seem to get this right is in the mother/baby units at hospitals. When a mother has a new baby and prepares to go home, a caregiver will escort mom and baby by wheelchair to the front door of the hospital. As the car pulls up, the caregiver helps to make sure the new car seat is properly installed and helps mom (and dad) get the baby securely belted in.

New parents sincerely appreciate this fond farewell, so why don't we do something similar for all patients? Sometimes we do. And sometimes we don't. Sometimes it's the nurse. Sometimes it's an intern. Sometimes it's a volunteer. Sometimes it isn't anyone at all.

If GOOD is the enemy of GREAT, then SOMETIMES is the enemy of ALWAYS.

We should always remember that our last impression leaves a lasting impression. When I helped the valet team park cars at Rochester General Hospital, I always ended the conversation with "Thank you for choosing Rochester General Hospital. Do you need driving directions to your next destination?" Almost always the guests said "No, thank you." But the smile on their face told me they appreciated the nice good-bye. I wasn't just parking cars. I was seeking to create fond farewells as the last part of the care team.

Note: For more Fond Farewells also see Lesson #90 Patient Belongings Bags

10

Connect by Asking Open-Ended Questions

I travel often for work, and I'm in and out of airports regularly. Once while at the Orlando airport preparing for a trip, I stopped in the airport Disney Store. I like to bring a few fun items as giveaways to some of my workshops, and as I started to make my way through the store, a cast member said, "Hi, welcome to the Disney Store. Where are you off to today?"

A question such as this will get more than the standard yes or no response. It's meant to be a conversation starter. I told her of my upcoming workshop in Kansas City and mentioned I was looking for some small, fun giveaways. As she walked me over to the bin with Mickey Mouse and Minnie Mouse figurines, she mentioned a favorite restaurant in Kansas City. Our conversation continued as I chose the items I wanted. She rang me up and then said, "Safe travels to Kansas City!"

> *We can never forget that our last impression leaves a lasting impression.*

May I help you?

When you visit most retail stores, the clerk typically asks, "May I help you?" Your answer is usually "No, I'm fine, thanks." But at Disney, cast members are trained to ask conversation starter questions such as, "Are you shopping for yourself today or looking for a gift?"

This is a communication technique that allows customers to answer with more information. This can also work with patients to elicit more than just a yes or no answer. Open-ended questions are designed to foster communication and increase engagement.

When used with patients, these kinds of questions can encourage patients to tell you more of their story, which may give you greater insight into their illness.

When used with team members, open-ended questions can lead to greater dialogue about job satisfaction, career goals, and other subjects.

11

Schedule for Courtesy and Compassion

People who go to Disney save up for the experience, and they expect to wait in line. In healthcare, people don't save and they don't expect to wait. The average American doesn't have between $4,000 - $6,000 in the bank to pay for their deductible. And, when they go to the emergency room, they're often asked to pay up front. It can be overwhelmingly stressful for patients and their families.

What's unique about Disney is that prior to opening a ride, hotel, or movie, they map out the ideal guest experience. Part of this planning involves asking "What's the ideal personnel to be cast in this role to ensure the seamless and flawless delivery of service, every time, ALWAYS? " Disney was creating a culture of always before Press Ganey or HCAHPS *(Hospital Consumer Assessment of Healthcare Providers and Systems)* were even thought of! A large percentage of guests who are in the parks have been there before and intend to return.

Unfortunately, healthcare has been scrutinized by budgets and productivity so much that they have scheduled so lean to the brink of danger. With the exception of cancer patients, heart patients, and new moms, I find that healthcare rarely sits down to design the ideal experience or schedule the ideal right-fit personnel needed to deliver the right experience over and over again. The main focus seems to be eliminating waste and inefficiencies and maximizing productivity at the expense of the patient experience.

At Disney, we discovered that courtesy and compassion can sometimes be very inefficient on the outset; if you skip it you will be faster and more efficient – but guests won't like you very much. And they won't come back.

So how do you correct the problem at your facility? Talk to patients about their experiences and wait times. Find out how long they are usually on hold, if it's hard to reach a nurse when they have a question, or if they receive timely follow up on test results. Once you identify the gaps in service, you can work with your team to move the focus back to the patient.

You'll likely find that small adjustments in scheduling lead to big changes in the overall patient experience.

12

Treat Patients as Guests

The original meaning of the word patient is 'one who suffers'. Does that term cover everyone who enters into a hospital? Should it define everyone we serve in healthcare? Of course we know that many patients are in pain, but not all. No two patients are exactly alike, and the individual is lost when we fail to see the whole person. This is also true for families, vendors, and visitors. Patients are our purpose, but are they our only customer?

If you want to create a culture of caring, you have to become intentional in your words and actions. When used with intention, words can invoke the right action. As we've previously described, the Walt Disney Company has an explicit language they use to intentionally focus their cast members on creating the ideal guest experience.

Disney does not call the people they serve *customers* because it sounds too transactional and impersonal. They call their customers GUESTS because cast members treat visitors as if they are guests in their own homes. The term guest implies that someone special was invited, and we want to make sure they are welcomed and well cared for. Having guests requires preparation. A giving and a receiving. It implies an interaction. Viewing patients as guests helps build lifelong relationships versus one-time transactions.

I recognize a hospital is not a hotel or theme park, and we are rarely going to call our patients and visitors "guests," but how do we create an attitude among everyone in our health system where we treat patients as we would guests in our own home? When we have guests in our home, we clean up a little extra... the hallways, the trash, and the bathrooms. We put out guest towels that we don't even allow our own family to use. So, in essence, we treat guests better than our own family members. Do we do the same for patients and visitors?

Everyone who enters a healthcare facility should be treated as a special guest. Guests at Disney Parks have choices. There are other entertainment options available. It's the same for patients and their family members today. Getting them in the door is easy, but getting them to want to come back can sometimes be hard. And we find that many times, the family member of the patient is the one filling out the patient satisfaction survey instead of the patient, so we need to be sure to include family members in the patient experience as well. Wouldn't it be great if visitors to any healthcare facility felt as welcomed guests rather than just visitors?

13

Proactively Seek Out Guest Contact

Have you ever wondered *how* Disney gets 74,000 cast members to be so consistently proactive and friendly? It's quite simple, actually - cast members know it's an expectation, not a suggestion.

Disney's Courtesy Behaviors

Within the heart of Disney's service strategy are Disney's Courtesy Behaviors, which all cast members are taught on day one. One of those behaviors is to seek out guest contact. Disney calls this being aggressively friendly. In other words, proactively approach guests *before* they approach you. Smile and greet them, first. Welcome them, and offer them great tips and best kept secrets on how to navigate the property. Help customize their vacation to meet their unique needs. And always offer to take their family photo (it may just be the only photo the chief family photographer is in). This behavior is simple, yet can be very impactful.

You can see this behavior manifest itself in retail and hospitality as well. Even some supermarkets do it.

Before I worked for Disney, I worked for Wegmans Supermarkets in Rochester, New York, where friendly employees are a company hallmark. Great supermarket chains have operationalized the concept of "seeking out guest contact" with their cashiers. It is now common to witness cashiers who have no current customers to come out from behind their registers, walk to the front of their check-out lane, and proactively invite customers, saying, "Good afternoon, ma'am, are you ready to check out now? Well, I can help you right here!"

Yet, in many of the competitor stores, without great training, those same cashiers would never leave their cash registers... happy for the respite and some free time to check their text messages and Facebook account. Those of us who specialize in the customer service industry refer to these employees as "minimalists." It's not that they are bad people, but without a connection to the purpose of their organization, the service philosophy and specific rules of engagement are noticeably missing. Minimalists tend to be reactive and comfortable in doing the least amount of work possible.

At Chick-Fil-A restaurants, managers "round" on customers in the dining areas and offer to refill drinks for free and clean up trash. They proactively seek out guest contact. What do you think people say about Chick-Fil-A when they get into their car, or to their friends and family?

At Marriott Courtyard hotels, front desk employees now stand at a kiosk instead of sitting behind a long front desk like so many of their competitors. Why? So they can more easily greet guests. Removing the physical barrier of the desk allows for a more human connection.

When you visit Las Vegas, check out their check in process at The Cosmopolitan of Las Vegas hotel. It is literally art in motion. A 150 foot-long front desk is broken up into eight-foot sections, allowing personnel to briefly leave their post and walk right up to the queue line. This provides them with direct access to 60-80 guests waiting to check in, and allows them to literally escort the next customer in line to the desk. It is something to marvel at and makes me wonder why we don't we do this in healthcare.

Just walk into any emergency room in America and there are typically two people sitting behind the front desk: a front desk clerk and a security officer. Both are always sitting, always busy, and RARELY proactive. Couldn't they be proactively friendly, too?

One truism that all healthcare leaders must always remember:

"Patients aren't just comparing us against other hospitals or clinics, they are comparing us against their other life experiences."

How our future patients get treated every day at their local Starbucks, Apple Store, supermarket or Chick-Fil-A matters to the expectations they will have of us. Those who pay attention and constantly seek to improve will thrive. Those who ignore this concept, and don't strive for continuous improvement, will eventually get left behind.

14

Offer Pleasant Little Surprises

When I went through leadership development training at Disney University (DU), my mentors taught me all about evidence-based data. Disney loves to mine data! "Know your guests," said Dennis Frare, my favorite mentor at DU. We knew a lot about the demographics of our guests: we knew where they came from, whether they flew or drove, their eating and spending habits, etc. We also knew that an average Disney guest would save up for two to three years to afford their Disney vacation. So expectations were very high that they would get their money's worth.

Another thing we learned from mining data was that an average guest would interact with 60-70 Disney cast members during the course of their vacation. That is 60-70 opportunities to make or break their overall impression of the value of that vacation. Dennis taught us that the goal of each of these interactions shouldn't necessarily focus on getting a 'wow' but instead to help fellow cast members to achieve an "oh" reaction from our guests:

"Oh, I didn't expect that."

"Oh, what a nice little thing that is."

What I have learned about customer service from analyzing the patient experience over the past decade is that deep inside all of us, we seem to have an Italian gene, and when somebody pleasantly surprises us, sometimes that Italian gene kicks in, and we say, "Oh..That's-A-NICE!" At Disney, you are going to interact with 60-70 folks this week…and when you start to string together these many pleasant little surprises, ("Oh.That's-A-NICE!") the end result is a "WOW!" "Wow, what do they put in the water at Disney?" "Wow! This place is amazing!" Many times we find that *Wow* is not one random act of kindness, but rather the sum of our pleasant surprise-interactions over time.

For example, if you leave your child's favorite stuffed animal in your Disney hotel room while you go out to the parks to play, you might just come back to find Pluto tucked in under the bed covers with his head on the pillow; or perhaps you'll find him sitting up on the bed watching the Disney channel with the TV remote in his paws. The next night you may find Mickey Mouse in the bathroom with a toothbrush in his hands and wearing a shower cap.

And do Disney housekeepers fold the ends of toilet paper rolls into triangles? You bet! Do they turn every day towels and wash clothes into Disney character origami? Of course. That too has been hard wired. Disney housekeepers are not only paid to learn towel origami, but it is now an expectation on their job description and performance review. Do you have housekeepers? Do they clean 16-18 rooms per day? Are they seeking to pleasantly surprise your guests…and get them to say, "Oh..That's-A-NICE!"?

Again, healthcare is not Disney. Most often healthcare delivery is not fun and it is not entertaining. People do not plan to be in a hospital, they didn't save for a triple bypass or kidney transplant, yet they want the same level of service wherever they are.

Sometimes the "oh" we create in healthcare can be created by just helping to remove the fear, anxiety, trepidation, and surprise. Instead of giving directions to help a distraught mother trying to find her son in the pediatric emergency room, could we escort her there? Instead of calling every patient by their last name, is it possible that we could ask the patient "what name would you like us to call you while you're here?" and then get our entire care team to use that name? How might that make our patient "Betty" feel if we actually pulled that off?

> **Wow! Is the sum of pleasant surprise interactions over time.**

15

Celebrate Life's Important Moments

Have you ever been sick on your birthday? It stinks, doesn't it? Well, now imagine being in the hospital on your birthday. Imagine that you are sick, scared, and perhaps even being prepped for major surgery. Can that get any worse? Sure it can. Imagine if all the multitude of care team members who enter your room, one right after the other, keep asking, "can you tell me your date of birth?" while doing safety checks. And what if that same month and day of your birth was TODAY, and no one wished you a happy birthday?

Come on, we have got to get this fixed! Reactively celebrating is one thing, but we also need to be proactively anticipating these kinds of events; after all, we have access to patient medical records and we know their date of birth.

When we miss celebrating life's important moments, it shows a lack of humanity.

As part of my company's work in hospitals and physician offices, we often act as mystery shoppers, pretending to be a patient or visitor to see how the experience feels to the average person. Once, dressed in jeans and a t-shirt, I eagerly walked up to the hospital's main information desk and said to a security guard working there, "Hi! My sister just had a baby! Can you tell me where to find the mother-baby floor?"

With no expression on his face at all, he looked up at me and said, matter of factly, "I'm gonna need your drivers license."

Confused, I replied, "My what?"

"Drivers License," he said, "That's a secure floor. You'll get it back when you give me back this ID Badge." he said as he handed me a clip-on visitor badge.

In any other part of planet Earth, what would any other human being say to you if you said, "Hey, my sister just had a baby!"? They would try to meet you at your energetic attitude and say, "HEY! CONGRATULATIONS! Did your sister have a boy or a girl?"

And if the Disney Security team ran your front desk, they would most likely offer you special ways to help celebrate that moment, all with a giant smile: A symbolic candy cigar, or a button that says PROUD UNCLE, for example. Then they would explain their work protocols - how they want to do everything to protect your sister and new niece, so everyone who goes on that floor needs a special badge.

Imagine how deflated visitors to the mother-baby unit must feel with the current process.

When we miss celebrating life's important moments, it shows a lack of humanity.

One of my family's favorite places to celebrate a birthday is at Chef Mickey's restaurant at Disney's Contemporary Resort hotel. There's nothing better than having dinner with Mickey Mouse and friends! We recently celebrated our son's birthday there, and when we told our server it was his special day, she made sure he received a birthday card signed by all the Disney characters.

Of course, the card was on hand for just such an occasion, but my son didn't know the character signatures were already there. To him, it was "Disney magic!"

People don't change when they're in the hospital. They still have birthdays, anniversaries, and other significant events in their lives.

You and your team can easily make a little magic for your patients with pre-made or pre-signed birthday cards. You already know their birth date (it's right on their electronic medical record), so why not take this little bit of personal information and create some magic? Birthday cards pre-signed by your care team can bring smiles to all patients – young and old at heart!

TIP: You may also want to consider having pre-made or pre-signed greeting cards on hand for anniversaries, encouragement, or sympathy.

16

Use the Famous Disney Two-Finger Point

When you work at the Walt Disney World Resort, you are working on a property the same size as San Fransisco. Working together with others, you help entertain millions of people each year.

Imagine how many people you give directions to each and every day! Every cast member learns the proper way to point to help guests navigate the property: it is the famous two-finger Disney point (or an open palm gesture). In many cultures, pointing with one finger can be considered rude. So when giving directions, Disney cast members are trained to use an open palm gesture or a two-finger point using the first and second fingers. Both offer a friendly and non-confrontational way to provide helpful information to guests from all over the world.

Wayfinding

In the complex world of healthcare, giving proper wayfinding directions is often overlooked. Many hospitals have become large and highly complex over the years as the need to treat more patients has dictated more specialized services and more patient wings to be built. Although it is always best to escort visitors to where they need to go, many employees in healthcare are not always able to leave their post for safety reasons, so it's appropriate to just point the way to their requested destination.

Now that you know that pointing with one finger can be seen as impolite, offer directions with the two-finger point. It doesn't take any extra time and it's one more way to show your human kindness to patients and visitors.

To patients, that is the real magic.

17

Let Them Hear a Smile in Your Voice!

I have always taught my employees that it is not just what you say, it's how you say it. When you are on the phone with someone, you can tell when they hate their job by the tone of their voice, can't you? You will become more liked and more believable if you put a smile in your voice.

It is much easier to put a smile in your voice when you're face to face with someone, right? All you have to do is literally smile! But it is extremely difficult to put a smile in your voice if you do not have a smile on your face. Try this experiment: look into a mirror, and with a frown on your face, try to say this with a smile in your voice, "It's a magical day at the Walt Disney World Resort. This is Jake, how may I help you, today?" Made you laugh, didn't it? It's hilarious because it's impossible!

Disney cast members who handle a multitude of incoming calls each day are trained to answer the phone by putting a smile in their voice. These employees are often the very first point of contact for guests and new employees. If you think about it, people considering a Disney vacation are about to invest thousands of dollars, and that first phone call could make or break that decision. So, do these frontline call center cast members know their title is really "Director of First Impressions?" In many world-class organizations, they do. But what about your healthcare facility? Consider the team members who answer your phones day in and day out. They handle calls for your customers, your employees and your physicians. Are they creating the warm welcome your patients and employees desire? Can you hear a smile in their voice?

How do you put a smile in your voice? Simply smile as you speak on the phone. It's easy to do, and your voice will automatically lilt upward and sound friendlier and more personable. Many service friendly call center employees hang mirrors from their computer monitors so they can see themselves smile. It is nearly impossible to put a smile in your voice if you do not have a smile on your face.

> *Remember, it's not just what you say, it's how you say it.*

TIP: Create phone message pads for all employees where the phrase **"Put a Smile In Your Voice"** is on the top as a reminder for all employees to provide exceptional service, even over the phone. Believe it or not, "Put a Smile in your Voice" was actually the name of one of the classes required for those who worked at Disney's call centers.

Remember that sincerity and authenticity is intentional. Some of your employees who answer the phones sound like they have already quit, but forgot to leave. That's why they sound like robots...or worse. The two best ways to get their humanity back is first to help them put a smile in their voice, and second, to treat them exactly like you want them to treat your patients. So in other words, leader, put a smile in your own voice.

18

The Power of a Warm Towel

The Japanese tradition of offering a warm hand towel to weary travelers or guests started long ago as a gesture of comfort and hospitality.

Many airlines and restaurants offer a warm towel to guests and passengers as a courtesy, and I believe it's something we can and should do in healthcare. There are outside companies that offer the service and the cost is minimal. All you need are your existing hand or washcloths, a microwave, and a little rosewater if you can.

Imagine you've just brought your grandmother to the emergency room for chest pain. It was a scary and frightening ordeal, but she's stable now and resting in her hospital bed. Then, someone brings her a warm, wet hand towel. It serves no clinical purpose, but as she uses it to clean her face and hands, she begins to feel like herself again. In fact, the warm hand towel may also help lower stress and anxiety in the patient, which may help her sleep and may even help with clinical outcomes.

When my uncle was hospitalized he got chilled towels because he was sweating, and he loved them. And when my grandmother put a hot towel to her face, she would smile. Even when she was in a coma and her eyes were glazed over, it made her smile.

19

Make Vendors Part of Your Care Team

Cast members who work in the Disney parking lots do more than just park cars. Not only do they offer local directions and tips for visiting the park, they also answer questions such as, "How late is the park open? Can I leave and return on the same day without paying an additional parking fee? Where can I find Mickey?"

They're also there at the end of the day to help find lost cars or help with a flat tire, dead battery, or a lockout. Clearly, they do more than just park cars.

The same thing is true of your parking lot attendants, valet parking team, and security officers. Do they know their role in the patient experience?

When patients arrive at your hospital or clinic, are the signs clearly marked? Is the parking lot clean and free of debris, trash, and obstacles? Are the parking attendants dressed appropriately and ready to greet patients? Do they welcome patients and visitors in a way that fits with your organization's culture?

Your "first impressions team" includes parking lot, valet, and security team members…and they can *and should* welcome patients and visitors to your facility because they're often the first face patients see. Do they know how important they are to the patient experience? If not, tell them! They do more than just park and retrieve cars; their role is to start (and end) the patient experience in a positive and exceptional way.

20

Apologize Immediately and With Empathy

Many leaders feel like they can't properly plan their day because they are always putting out fires, moving from one to the next without predictability. We're all human, and eventually all humans make mistakes. So the question is not whether you will make a mistake, but what will you do when it happens. Regardless of whether the mistake was your fault or not, service recovery is always a valuable way to turn a negative situation into a positive one.

Things can and will go wrong, even at the happiest place on Earth. And when they do, Disney cast members are trained on how to resolve the situation. It starts with the right **intentional** words to use and avoid. For example, there are no "problems, issues or complaints" at Disney; there are only "guest situations or concerns." "Situations and concerns" are great non-blame, middle of the road phrases that are least likely to elevate anxieties.

After listening to the guest's concern, the next step in the service recovery process is to offer a sincere apology. An apology isn't necessarily an admission of guilt or wrongdoing; it's simply a way of showing compassion and empathy toward the guest while continuing to work towards a resolution. It might sound like this: "I am so sorry that happened to you. If that had happened to me, I'd be upset, too. Let me see what I can do to resolve this for you."

Doctors, nurses, and other healthcare professionals are all human. Patients know this intuitively, but they sometimes forget. Clinical and operational excellence is always the goal, but occasionally, mistakes get made. Sometimes they're medical in nature, but often times they are not. Sometimes, it's just the patient's perception of what

> *The patient is not always right (and is often wrong), but they should always be treated with dignity and respect.*

happened. Since perception is reality, we should always remember the patient is not always right (and is often wrong and confused), but they should always be treated with dignity and respect. Regardless of who was right or wrong, patients are much more forgiving if an apology is immediate, sincere, and if there is also some kind of small "I'm sorry" token to help smooth things over as you seek to fix what went wrong (these could include an "I'm sorry" card, sympathy card, flowers, gas card, or even a meal coupon to your cafe).

Whether they're right or wrong, we still want to make the right LASTing impression (LAST is the Disney acronym for Service Recovery: Listen, Acknowledge and Apologize, Solve, and Thank.)

Listen with your eyes and with your whole body.

Acknowledge by repeating back what you heard them say and **Apologize**.

Solve, if you're able.

Thank them.

Build a Learning Process

Regardless of the symbolic atonement gift(s) that go along with your sincere apologies, you must document these everyday situations and what you did to try to solve and avoid their recurrence. When you do this, you build an authentic learning *process* and not just an insincere bandaid station where one Starbucks coffee coupon fits all situations.

A strong service recovery process helps you become a learning organization. This process is one in which employees feel like they are truly empowered to own bad situations and make them right, whether it was their fault or not, and whether it was within their control or not. Remember, if you notice a situation that needs to be addressed, **you own it**. If you don't build a process of ownership, your employees will just continue to send unhappy customers or patients to a complaint department or to their manager (which just makes it worse when they have to tell their story all over again).

Keep in mind that sometimes people don't really want anything more than just to be heard and the assurance that it won't happen again to someone else. Sometimes all they need to hear is "I'm sorry that happened." Empathy is an important part of Service Recovery.

The goal to a Service Recovery process is to do more than just fix the problem. The next step is to share it with your team and develop a permanent fix. You want to capture it and share it with your team so it never happens again.

21

Proactively Anticipate Guest Situations

When I worked at Disney, we had a team of locksmiths called "Key Control" who roamed the parking lots of the theme parks at closing time just in case guests locked their keys in the car. Why? Because more than 2,000 people lock their keys in their car at Disney every year.

Imagine you are on the last day of a four-day Disney vacation. You just spent 15 glorious hours (and every penny saved) at Epcot. It's now midnight. One of your children is asleep on your shoulder, another asleep in a stroller. You get to your car only to find out that your keys are locked inside! Distressed, exhausted, and frustrated, you flag down a Disney Security Officer and she radios the Key Control dispatch. Two gentlemen show up in an unmarked white van and POOF! Within a few minutes, they magically retrieve your keys from the car. When they ask you to start the car, it's then you find out the battery is also dead and the gas tank is on empty because you left the car running all day long! "No problem," they say. "We have you covered." Between the Key Control team and the Security Officer, they have jumper cables ready to assist with a dead battery and a portable gas can for the occasional empty gas tank.

It's not the Disney cast member's fault that someone left their lights on, ran their battery down, or ran out of gas. But by proactively anticipating guest challenges or situations that might arise, Disney cast members have the opportunity to become **Service Heroes**.

Think about it: you just spent thousands of dollars on a vacation of a lifetime and everyone seemed to have a great time, but your last memory of that wonderful vacation is that **you** locked the keys in the car...and you left the car running! That could have easily ruined your entire vacation. But not at Disney.

Create Your Own Service Heroes

Now, think of where you work. Does your hospital or medical facility have similar situations with guest parking or vehicles? And do you have a plan in place? Can you think of some things that aren't your fault, but are major patient or visitor dissatisfiers? Do you have a process to help people find lost items such as eye glasses or dentures? Is there a plan in place for when you find out today is your patient's birthday? What happens when someone shows up three hours early or three hours late for their appointment? What happens when an elderly grandmother is dropped off at your facility by her grandson, only to find out she is at the wrong location, her grandson's cell phone is dead, and will not be back for another two hours?

Is there anything you can do? Anyone you can call? Patients <u>know</u> these things aren't your fault, but can you become the hero? Imagine how pleasantly surprised they'll be when you have anticipated their needs and have an immediate solution prepared and already in place.

One night, my wife brought our 10 year-old daughter to the emergency room in the middle of the night. I was out of town and my wife had to shoulder this emergency on her own. Unfortunately, our daughter became physically sick in the car as they were on their way. When they arrived at the emergency room entrance, the valet parking attendant was able to help get a wheelchair, but when my wife asked if there was anyone they could call to help clean her car, the response was, "No, ma'am, we just park cars." As helpful as the valet attendant was with everything else, he simply had no solution for my wife's dilemma. Now what if that car was going to sit in that parking garage for two days? Yuck!

It's not the valet attendant's fault our daughter became ill and threw up all over the back seat of our car. But wouldn't it have been nice if the hospital partnered with a local car detailing company to assist patient vehicles in just such a situation? Being that this happened at the entrance of a hospital emergency department, do you think this situation has ever happened before? Do you think it will ever happen again? Of course! The question becomes what can the valet team do to respond more helpfully the next time? With a variety of solutions in place, can you see how they could easily become the hero in the end?

Part of the magic of Disney is that they have a plan in place for almost any event imaginable. When you fill a person full of popcorn, soda, and Mickey Mouse Ice Cream bars, and place them on a roller coaster or spinning tea cup, accidents happen! Disney has a secret code to use when communicating over walkie talkie radios to maintain the integrity of the show and avoid embarrassment for park guests.

There are numerous ways to anticipate and prepare for patient and family situations in healthcare. Many of the circumstances will be different, but opportunities to proactively address situations before they occur are easy to anticipate with a bit of practice and a slight change in mindset.

I discovered an excellent example when I worked with Riverside Health System in Newport News, Virginia. When a victim of sexual assault goes to the hospital for treatment, the standard protocol to gather evidence is to take all of their articles of clothing, which leaves the victim dressed in a paper gown feeling vulnerable, cold, and further victimized. This means that women, men and children are leaving our hospitals in paper scrubs after a moment of greatest trauma.

To lessen the emotional trauma of this process, Riverside Health System has Fear 2 Freedom kits.

F2F Kits are a gift of hope given to victims of abuse when they arrive at the hospital. These kits include new items such as:

- Appropriately sized t-shirt, sweatpants, and undergarments

- Toiletries, including soap, shampoo, conditioner, a toothbrush, toothpaste, a loofah, and a hairbrush

- A pen and journal for adults and a toy for children

- "You Matter 2" card (includes list of sponsors)

- Resource card (list of help lines and tips)

- Freedom Bear

- Personal, handwritten note (written by a student or volunteer)

F2F Kits are assembled by college students at special events throughout the year. For each event, F2F partners the university or college with a hospital and/or community organization for which F2F Kits will be supplied. Beth Walters, a Forensic Nurse at Riverside Health System, recently told us, "*I cannot imagine doing the PERK exam without these F2F Kits.*"

22

Have a Plan for Lost Items

Every day, guests lose thousands of personal items at the Walt Disney World Resort. It should come as no surprise that Disney has a plan in place to help deal with these lost items and to also proactively avoid the losses in the first place.

When people are on vacation, they get out of their daily routine and often leave things behind. Lost articles include everyday items such as eyeglasses, sunglasses, cell phones, and chargers. Many times, the lost items have extreme emotional value, such as jewelry given from a deceased relative. They also include autograph books filled with personal notes from the Disney characters that children spent their entire vacation collecting. Disney has a very organized process to help guests retrieve their lost items.

If you have your name and mailing address on your lost item, you might be surprised when Disney mails your found item home to you. And sometimes, you may even find a note inside your lost item box signed by Mickey Mouse (pre-printed, of course)! This too becomes an incredible, pleasant surprise and personal touch.

Disney has a very robust lost and found process in place. Every day of the year, all lost items that are found are tagged, boxed and shipped to Disney's Central Lost and Found. From there, items are logged and held between 30 - 90 days, depending on their value.

Proactively anticipating and avoiding the loss of personal items is another solution. The last time my family and I checked out of Disney's Wilderness Lodge, the bellman who came to pick up our luggage asked, "Mr. Poore, I will take all these bags down to your car for you...now, did you get all your cell phone and kids game chargers?" This is part of his Disney script. And thank goodness he asked because I had forgotten the cell phone charger I had left plugged into an outlet in the room.

The 87 year-old father of my good friend, Brian Wong, was in the hospital. Mr. Wong was taken from his hospital room to the radiology department for a procedure. When Mr. Wong returned to his room he discovered that housekeeping had cleaned the room, changed his beds sheets, and inadvertently lost his dentures in the process! Why is that important? Mr. Wong literally could not chew food without his dentures. And over time he lost his interest to eat. Eventually his gums receded, requiring painful, expensive surgery - and it all began because of an innocent mistake made by a well-meaning team member. My point is, you must have a process for everyday situations like these.

What process do you have in your hospital or medical office for lost items? I'm always unpleasantly surprised by the number of organizations that have no proactive process in place at all. For most hospitals, valuables are either stored with the housekeeping supervisor or kept in a safe with Security. Many times Environmental Services (housekeeping) has a cardboard box in their break room where they throw inexpensive lost items, but there's typically no formal process to label, log, and return lost items back to their patients. Isn't that ironic? We know everything about the patient (name, address, ailments, medications, insurance company, phone number, cell number, and next of kin), yet we can't seem to proactively call them and tell them they left something behind...much less mail it to them before they call.

Leadership

"The greatest challenge in healthcare isn't

meeting or exceeding expectations;

it's that we don't set them."

- Jake Poore

23

Set Expectations So You Can Exceed Them

Walt Disney World theme park operations became famous for setting clear expectations by posting the estimated wait time at the beginning of each of their attractions. If you measure the time you actually waited, you will find your wait is often shorter than the estimated wait time posted on the sign. They do this so they can <u>set</u> your expectations and then **exceed** your expectations.

Of course, Disney can do this because their attractions run on a predictable time table and your world in healthcare is anything but predictable, right? Not everything. When we get into a rhythm, we can be very predictable.

I find one of the greatest challenges in healthcare isn't that we fail to meet and exceed expectations; it's that we often fail to SET expectations at all. For example, over the last 15 years, I've been asking healthcare leaders and employees in the emergency department - "what is the average time it takes to get test results back from the lab from a patient's blood or urine sample?" They tell me the average turnaround time is between 60-90 minutes. But my next question gets some stares and scoffs. "So then, what do we tell the patient how long it will be?"

Patients tell us the top three typical responses they get from emergency room employees are:

#1 response: "They don't tell us anything. So we are just left to wonder (and stew)."

#2 response: "They say they'll be back shortly." And most patients think *shortly* means just a few minutes.

#3 response: "They say the results will be back *soon.*" Which most people think is no more than 10 minutes.

So when you actually come back with the results in 90 minutes, have you exceeded the patient's expectations, met their expectations, or fallen short? Consider trying the Disney way. Set your self up for success and overestimate the time a bit so that you can exceed their expectations.

Many emergency room personnel are reluctant to share any time stamp because "things come up and sometimes other urgent tests get prioritized over your test." This is true, but is the exception. When that happens, just be sure to circle back to the patient at the time you told them to expect the results and explain why their test is taking longer.

Patients don't necessarily mind waiting as much they hate not being kept in the loop.

For patients, it feels like the captured prisoner syndrome, where the people in charge only tell you what they want you to know. But when you set clear expectations for patients, you help set a time stamp in their head so now they can do something else rather than just sit there and wonder, watching the clock and growing more frustrated as time passes.

24

Cultivate an Ownership Attitude

One of Disney's well-known differentiators is having cast members who take ownership of situations that are presented to them. Not only do cast members seem incredibly knowledgeable, but they go out of their way to find the information they don't have, and rarely send you on a wild goose chase to try find it by yourself. Whether it's trash on the ground, helping a lost child find their family, or providing service recovery, at Disney, when someone brings you an opportunity, you don't say "I don't know" or "It's not my job." Cast members actively seek out the solution.

Why? Because that is the clearly defined culture. They not only have clearly delineated what they stand for; they also outline what they will not stand for. Everything that creates the ideal "show" or experience is what Disney calls, "good show," and anything that detracts or distracts away from a good Disney show is called, "bad show." Sounds simple right? Sometimes in business, you have to be brilliant on the basics.

At Disney, on your first day of work you immediately learn that saying, "It's not my job" is bad show. It is absolutely appropriate to start a response with "I don't know..." but then end it with "but let me find out for you." The promise I made to all new cast members when I taught "Disney Traditions" (Disney's new employee orientation program) was "If you find out the answer to a question, any question, the next time someone asks you that same question - you'll be the expert!" And today, Disney has a world-class reputation for having very friendly, knowledgeable employees. The key to gaining knowledge is the willingness to find the answer. And willingness is tied to attitude. That is why Disney hires for attitude and trains for skill.

I was consulting at National Rehabilitation Hospital where we created a concept called the "no passing zone." If you traveled through a high occupancy patient waiting area, you had to give one person eye contact, smile, and say hello. You couldn't pass through the zone without saying good morning to at least one person.

This concept then morphed to the medical-surgical floor, where if you walked past a room and saw a call light illuminated – whether you were clinical or not and whether you worked on that floor or not – if you saw it, you owned it. Anyone can enter a typical patient room and say, "Good morning, I saw your call light, may I help you?" Most times, it's not a clinical request at all. Perhaps they just can't find their eyeglasses, or the TV remote, or they dropped the book they were reading.

In healthcare today, we do not tend to reward people for taking this kind of initiative.

Remember, no passing the buck. When you are given a patient request during a no passing zone moment and you delegate it to someone else, you still own the follow-up to ensure it gets done. Your good name is the one on the line, not the person you delegated to.

> **Remember, if you see it, hear it, or smell it – you own it.**

25

Lead By Example

Even before I worked at Disney, I learned an important lesson from my father who used to say, "If it's meant to be, it starts with me!" And then I saw it in action at Disney.

I could share many stories with you about leading by example, but the most memorable one to me involves Dick Nunis, former President of Walt Disney World. He was visiting Disney's Contemporary Resort in the afternoon before its grand opening in 1971. The grass sod had not yet been laid, and it was starting to get dark. It was a big deal because not only was the world wide press going to be there, but Bob Hope was coming the next day to be the master of ceremonies for the grand opening. Dick, who was famous for wearing business suits and white shoes, rolled up his sleeves and yelled, "I want to help. What can I do?" The general contractor simply yelled back, "Green side up!" A simple order was all it took for Dick to jump in!

Green Side Up!

Cast members subsequently went up to Dick as he was laying sod and asked, "How can I help?" His reply was, "Green side up!" Soon, many others jumped in to lay sod, and the process continued throughout the night. When a new person arrived they were told, "Green side up!"

This is a terrific example of a leader leading by example. That phrase became a mantra at Disney for leaders to be hands on and jump in to help whenever needed.

The same can be true in healthcare. When I was at Ochsner Clinic in 2004, I was in the basement of the hospital, heading down the hall to visit with the maintenance supervisor, when I passed by the laundry department. There was a bulletin board marking the entrance to the laundry department that had photographs plastered all over it. When I looked closely at some of the photographs, I noticed that the CEO, Dr. Pat Quinlan, and the President, Warner Thomas, were in green scrubs working side-by-side with laundry personnel folding towels and sheets.

Curious to know when this was, I walked into the laundry department and said to the employees, "That's great! Your CEO and President were here recently! I saw the photograph on the wall. When was that photograph taken?" And they said, "That photograph was taken seven years ago." I said, "Why is that photograph still on the board then, if it was seven years ago?" And they said, "We will never take that photograph down. We love the fact that they visited here to understand what we do and how we do it."

26

Catch 'Em Doing Things Right

Let's play fill in the blank.

"Good news travels fast. Bad news travels _____."

You probably finished that sentence by saying, "Bad news travels *faster.*"

It's true.

Many leaders pass bad news down the chain of command, and by the time it gets to you it's spread like wildfire.

Let's try another one.

"The only time I really see or hear from my boss is when I do something _____."

Did you say *wrong*? When asked, employees will typically say that the only time they hear from their leader is when they're doing something wrong. But unfortunately, sometimes that's all that leaders and supervisors talk about or have time for: the wrong. If you think about it, bad things get formally documented; good things don't.

Healthcare leaders today have an enormous amount of responsibility (many departments, many employees) and typically no formal, on-the-spot recognition program to capture good deeds in action.

> **Surprise your team by catching them doing something right!**

Why not surprise your team by catching them doing something right? Before going up to a floor, call ahead to find out what good things have been going on so you can celebrate them when you get there. Even if you're bringing bad news, try to point out three positives for every negative comment.

It sets a new environment and tone for your team members by rewarding positive behavior.

And it can also create momentum where every employee wants to be recognized for doing the right thing.

In the end, many employees don't feel appreciated, as if they have to find their own reward in the work they do. So as leaders, our number one job should be creating a culture of appreciation by celebrating life's moments in the moment, rather than waiting until the end of the month, the end of the quarter or year, or worse, the end of their career.

If you want to create a world-class culture, start by creating a culture of appreciation.

I find the greatest challenge in healthcare regarding recognition programs is typically they're an 'above and beyond' program. Above and beyond what? We don't have a standard departmental playbook that includes both operational and service protocols so how can we know what above and beyond is? In the outset, we make it subjective. And when it's subjective, it loses credibility. It's my manager's opinion against mine.

My favorite example of an entire organization that is aligned towards a common theme, "We create happiness," is when my best friend and I were getting ready to tee off on the first tee of the Lake Buena Vista Golf Course at Walt Disney World, where we noticed a dozen guys smoking cigars at 7:00 AM, clearly celebrating something. Our curiosity drew us toward them, and at about the same time a greenskeeper, driving a huge circular lawnmower, noticed the men, too.

So the landscaper, my buddy and I all converged on the group. The greenskeeper turned off his lawnmower, took his safety headgear off, and asked what the big celebration was. One of the guys said, "It's Tony's 50th birthday, and we all flew in to celebrate the occasion." The greenskeeper then said, "Happy birthday, Tony! You know, I have not yet picked the pin placement for the 18th hole. Would you like to pick it, since today is your birthday?" And Tony exclaims, "Would I?!" And out goes the group of guys, one birthday boy and 11 paparazzi, stocked with Kodak film, to pick the pin placement for the day. A barrage of photos ensues while Tony lays on the green pointing to the exact spot for the perfect pin placement for the 18th hole flag.

The greenskeeper asks one of Tony's friends for his camera, and says, "You know, our Pro Shop develops film. I would love it if we could develop the film in your camera so we could have those photographs when you get off the course today. I'll do it as my birthday gift to Tony." The trusting friend hands over the camera, and the greenskeeper, after cutting the hole for the 18th green, takes the camera to the shop and gets the film developed. He takes one of the developed pictures, blows it up on the photocopy machine, writes "Happy birthday Tony from Toledo, Ohio!" on the top, puts it in plexiglass, and places it at the 18th tee box where people tee off.

When Tony and his friends get to the 18th tee box, they are blown away to find a sign that says, "Today's pin placement was picked by Tony from Toledo, Ohio. Happy birthday, Tony."

I wrote that greenskeeper up on a Disney Service Fanatic Card, their internal recognition process, for going above and beyond.

The story was selected for Disney's internal newsletter called *Walt Disney World Eyes & Ears* for 74,000 cast members. The superintendents of Disney's golf courses got together and asked the very basic question, "Why can't we do this every day?" Now, this has become standard operating protocol. It is a great example of a random act of kindness that became business as usual due to an on-the-spot recognition process.

One random act of kindness in healthcare that has now been standardized and embraced is when cancer patients graduate from all of their chemotherapy treatments, they get to ring a ship captain's bell to celebrate the momentous occasion. But where did that come from? It was probably started by one employee who had a great idea to bring a bell to work to help her patients celebrate something difficult, yet rewarding. Someone wrote up the story, it was shared in an employee newsletter, and some administrator said, "Why can't we do this for all cancer patients?"

27

Listen to Your Employees

I've seen research studies suggesting that 67% of all business problems can be solved by asking your employees. Employees have the solutions to most management questions, but managers rarely ask.

Have you ever lost your car at a Disney theme park? It's easy to do when you consider there are more than 40,000 parking spots at Walt Disney World parks and resorts. If you want something fun to do, come to the Disney parking lot after the fireworks and watch families try to find their car after spending 12 hours in the park that day. We could hold divorce court right at the main exit at Epcot to help save marriages and keep families together!

It was Disney cast members who created a solution to an age-old problem of finding lost cars.

When I started at Disney 30 years ago, you had two options for finding your car. You could either sit with your family under a palm tree and wait for the parking lot to empty, or you could wander down each row, one at a time, until you found your car. Either way, you left Disney with a bad taste in your mouth. Occasionally, Disney security officers would throw your family into their station wagon and at least drive you down each row, but still the solution was not at hand.

One day a Disney front-line cast member who was working overtime that day simply asked the guest with a missing car what time they got to the park that day. The guest replied, "around 9:30

this morning." The cast member said, "I remember what rows were being parked around 9:30 AM – let me take you there."

And so it hit him. If we just wrote down the times we parked each row, and made photocopies of our log for the closing shift, we could set cast members up to be service heroes! (By the way, hospitals can offer a similar convenience by "naming" parking lots and numbering the parking spaces so patients and visitors can remember where they parked or take a quick photo.)

In healthcare, your employees see and hear things that you may not. Encourage them to come up with solutions that may make things more convenient for patients and visitors.

28

Embrace Diversity

When I worked at Walt Disney World, the phrase that could be found in every job posting was **"Drawing strength from diversity."**

The idea of having a wide variety of people within the Disney organization is seen as a competitive advantage. Walt Disney himself famously embraced diversity when, as the story goes, he asked a maintenance worker from Jamaica to ride with him through the unfinished Pirates of the Caribbean attraction. Walt reportedly asked what was missing from the famous night scene. The maintenance worker thought for a minute and then replied, "Fireflies." Walt made sure that there were little lights placed throughout the ride to simulate the fireflies a native Jamaican had noticed were missing.

In healthcare, having a diverse staff allows for a competitive advantage in language (translation, for example) and customs (having special foods available on holidays, perhaps) and can enhance the overall patient and employee experience.

By embracing those with different life experiences – including job histories – organizations remain more open to different, better ways of doing things through diversity of thought and ideas.

29

Celebrate the Intent, Coach the Behavior

One of the most valuable leadership lessons I learned at Disney was to help people understand their role in the show and give them a little leeway to express that role. If you have 74,000 people trying to create happiness and they don't have an instruction manual, allow them to try to create happiness in their own way.

Occasionally they'll get it wrong – but we need to celebrate the intent. The first step is to get employees to be purpose-driven and not job-task driven. You must get people to understand the difference between their job tasks and their role in creating the ideal experience. Second, encourage them to be creative in making the ideal experience come true. I've found that people will often pleasantly surprise you.

At one of our client's hospitals, a situation arose when a hospital care team member was escorting a patient in a wheelchair to the curb. To everyone's surprise, three feet of snow had fallen since the patient's arrival a few days prior.

The team member asked the patient where she parked her car. The patient pointed to a snow-covered car and said, "I believe it's under there." The team member said, "No problem. Let me take you back inside to stay warm, and I'll clean off your car. May I have your keys?" The patient was delighted.

Cleaning off the car and warming it up was absolutely no problem. But then the employee took it one step too far by driving the patient's car to the front door. She was the hero up until the point where she drove the patient's car because, in the hospital's eyes, that was a liability.

This employee needed to be recognized and celebrated for going above and beyond, and then privately coached that she just took it one step too far. If she was simply reprimanded for driving the car, she would have been discouraged from trying to go above and beyond in the future.

By celebrating the intent and coaching the behavior, employees will have the confidence and motivation to put their best foot forward on behalf of the patient.

30

Localize Your Culture

Once you articulate a global way of doing things (your Service Theme or True North) you need to localize it by department. If your team does not feel the overarching statement is appropriate, relevant, and authentic to them and their department, it will not help connect them to a purpose. The more you localize it by department, the more ownership people feel. There is power and alignment in a global statement, but real authenticity comes when it is localized.

Localize Your Global Service Theme/True North

Everyone at Walt Disney World follows the same global service theme, which is "We create happiness by providing the finest in entertainment for people of all ages, everywhere." Most cast members just remember and recite the first three words as a simple way of keeping the purpose in their minds at all times. However, many divisions of the organization "localize" the theme to make it more relevant and authentic to their specific division.

For example, at the Disney Vacation Club (vacation timeshare program), "We create happiness by allowing you to own a piece of the magic." At Disney transportation (buses, monorails, trains) they say, "We create happiness by keeping the magic moving." At Disney laundry services (supporting the world's largest working wardrobe), "We create happiness by the keeping the magic squeaky clean." At the Disney Institute it's, "We create happiness by allowing you to discover the business behind the magic."

Knowing the mission is just the first step. If employees don't know the why, the what doesn't matter, especially with the millennial generation. Employees need to understand how the work they do contributes to the bigger picture.

I was a consultant in one hospital where the sterile processing department team did not see their purpose. They actually saw themselves as "glorified dishwashers." So I asked them, "Do you realize without you sterilizing these instruments and fully assembling them exactly right into a surgical kit, patients could die?" Their response was, "I never really thought of it that way. And our managers have never really told it to us that way." And then I asked something that really blew their minds. "Have you ever seen your surgical kit in action in the operating room?" The unanimous answer was no. To me, this is like the seamstress who creates amazing costumes for the theater but never actually sees the show. It's like the animator who does the background animation for *The Little Mermaid* without ever seeing the movie.

So I asked, "Would you like to see your instruments being used in surgery?" And 80% of them said yes. So we started a monthly surgical shadowing program. Sterile processing team members would get to see a surgery of the surgical kit they themselves cleaned and assembled, and the quid quo pro was they had to come back to their team to tell their coworkers how their clean surgical kits were used to save a child's life, or were used in a hip replacement. So out of that the team came up with their own localized departmental service theme, **"We provide tools that save lives."**

Where would you rather work - in a place where you feel like a glorified dishwasher, or in a place where everyone feels like they clean and assemble surgical tools that save lives?

31

Your Role in the Show

Disney believes that every position is as important as every other position. A world-class singer or dancer is not going to do their best if the audio-visual team or sound techs don't do their jobs effectively.

In healthcare, a world-class surgeon cannot operate without the right surgical equipment, cleaned and assembled by the sterile processing team. Not everyone in the healthcare industry has direct contact with patients, but we all have an impact on the patient experience. An administrator in a satellite office working on coding can still trace his or her way back to the patient and how that patient is being cared for.

It is important that you remind your team that caregivers need to respect and take care of each other. A classic example in healthcare involves the world-class surgeon, Michael E. DeBakey, of Methodist Hospital in Houston, Texas. Dr. DeBakey was known for interacting with frontline employees as he walked through the hospital. One legendary example is when Dr. DeBakey stopped an elderly janitor in the hallway and asked him about his wife and children. He told the man, obviously not for the first time, that the hospital could not function without him as germs and infection would spread if it weren't for him and his team. Someone asked that same janitor later in the day, "What exactly do you do here?" And with immense pride, the janitor replied, "Dr. DeBakey and I – we save lives together."

32

Empower With Operational Priorities

Operational Priorities are a set of agreed-upon standards that are prioritized in order of importance to empower employees to make non-emergency decisions on the spot. Along with the True North statement, the Operational Priorities must also be in place to provide a practical blueprint of how every interaction should occur. They also serve as a decision-making filter for everyone to use when conflicts arise in the course of delivering service excellence to patients and to each other (our internal customers).

Walt Disney World's Service Theme begins with the words "We Create Happiness..." The "Four Keys" (or Operational Priorities) that help deliver on that promise are:

1. Safety

2. Courtesy

3. Show

4. Efficiency

It is always those four, and always in that order. Every department's priorities are the same, providing consistency and continuity across the entire 43 square miles of Walt Disney World property.

When everyone is working within a culture with a common set of operational priorities, and everyone is looking through the same lens, employees feel empowered and reassured that the organization has got their back. Using the Operational Priorities, every employee can analyze the situation for the best possible outcome and share that outcome or solution with all employees in their department and throughout the organization to ensure consistency of delivery. Ultimately, this becomes more than just service recovery to fix a problem or a random act of kindness. Instead it becomes systematized so that everyone in the healthcare system can say "this is the way we do things here in this organization."

For the past 17 years, my team and I have worked in more than 500 hospitals. We often ask employees if they have a guiding plan for what to do in every situation. Not surprisingly, the answer is almost always no.

Imagine if a morbidly obese patient insists that you (his nurse) help lift him and take him to the restroom immediately. The dilemma for the nurse is whether to take a personal and patient safety risk to avoid a complaint, OR, to honor this patient's urgent request.

Or do you explain to the patient that you need to get assistance from your team to help? Or offer a bed pan?

National data says that worker's compensation claims for injured nurses is at an all time high. Nurses who are concerned about patient complaints and patient satisfaction scores may risk their own personal safety in the pursuit of better scores.

Imagine you are on your way to a 9:00 AM meeting with the hospital CEO and the executive team. As you walk down the hallway you pass a visitor who is visibly lost and distraught over her failure to find their loved one, a patient in the ER. You are not sure if you should be efficient and get to the CEO's meeting on time, or be courteous and help this family member with complex directions, or offer to walk her to her destination, knowing full well you will be late to the meeting with the CEO. You wonder if the CEO and executive team will support your reason and forgive your lateness.

Now imagine that your organization has a set of Operational Priorities in place, with safety first, courtesy second, and efficiency last. Because you understand your organization's decision-making process, you know you can help the family member (courtesy) and arrive a little bit late to the meeting.

An everyday challenge faced by most hospital Unit Clerks happens many times each week. The clerk is already on the phone helping a patient who was discharged yesterday and is confused by the discharge instructions. At the same time, seven other patient call lights start ringing. One of those patients becomes so impatient at the lack of a response that he gets out of bed, grabs his IV pole, walks down the hall, and is now glaring at the Unit Clerk who is still on the phone. At the same time, a doctor walks up to the clerk, taps her on one shoulder and asks for a patient's chart, and a nurse also walks up, taps her on the other shoulder and asks her to fax a consultation request.

What does the Unit Clerk do next? Who does she serve first, second, and third? It would help if the Unit Clerk had a decision-making tool to help her prioritize the multiple requests demanding her attention.

At Integrated Loyalty Systems, we believe that your care team members need to help develop and prioritize standards that all team members will be able to use in making decisions for every day dilemmas. It is not a perfect science, but with a shared tool you can start a conversation to help find a common solution to recurring challenges. Eventually, every leader and front line team member can have a common set of tools and a common language that creates consistency in both thought and in action.

Employee Best Practices

"A good rule of thumb is to treat your employees

exactly as you would like them

to treat their patients."

- Jake Poore

33

Create a "Right Fit" Recruiting Video

Disneyland is famously known for being the original happiest place on earth. Much of that notoriety is due to the friendly employees who work there. Many business people have always wanted to know *how do you make your employees so happy?*

The honest answer has always been **Disney hires happy people.**

How does Disney find happy people to apply for jobs? One way they find happy people is by setting expectations before people interview for a job. Disney asks all applicants to watch a pre-employment video, which is short and to the point and clearly explains what Disney stands for and what Disney won't stand for.

A pre-employment video is an excellent way for career seekers to get a clear and concise idea about the culture of your organization. I firmly believe that unexpressed expectations can sometimes lead to unintended resentment.

Job seekers who click on the careers tab of your website should be able to view a short video that clearly describes your organization's history and heritage; the way you treat your patients and the way you treat each other, the non-negotiables of employment, and clear expectations of becoming an exceptional care team member.

General research has found that about ten percent of people who watch recruitment videos do not go forward with the application process. They self-select out because they realize the organization isn't a right fit for them. This is a win-win for everybody. Interviewers and the organization don't waste time on someone who is not a right fit, and the interviewee goes out and tells others for whom it would be a right fit. People who self-select out of your organization oftentimes unknowingly end up recruiting others to apply for work at the organization with clear expectations.

34

Improve Your New Hire Orientation

Ask any Disney cast member, past or present, if they remember their new employee orientation (NEO) and I guarantee you they'll say yes. Why? Because Walt Disney Company's "Traditions," is an outstanding new employee orientation program. It's an intensive (and fun!) full-day orientation that every cast member attends to learn about the culture, history, and significant milestones of the organization. But most importantly, it's a memorable first day for new cast members and sets the tone for a promising future.

Always remember that it's not what we say to new employees, rather it's how we make new people **feel** about the organization and their decision to become a new employee. It's where culture meets the customer. It's an emotional quotient.

Healthcare has relied on *see one, do one, teach one* onboarding for far too long. Most people who train employees are not certified as trainers. They often teach what they were taught in the form of, "Here's how I do it."

Take a moment to think about what *your* orientation program is like for new team members. Is it engaging and interactive? Does it seem like an endless parade of guest speaker after guest speaker? Or is simply a seminar on all the things you *don't* want new employees to do?

Here are the two key things to remember when redesigning your new employee orientation:

1. Make sure the content reflects your organizational message.

2. Deliver the content in a way that makes your new employees feel as welcomed and as well cared for as you want your patients to feel when they come to you for care.

Disney Trainers Program

My most memorable training event was the Disney Trainers program. The approach was brilliant! About 30 fellow cast members and I showed up to the class to learn how to become a Disney trainer, but when we arrived we discovered the classroom was dirty! The lights were half-off. The facilitator's shirt was hanging out. The room was the wrong temperature. There was no coffee. There were no slides on the screen. The materials were not organized. The trainer, who was chewing gum, didn't welcome us. He just told us to have a seat and that we would get started in a moment.

A few minutes later, another cast member poked his head in the room and said, "Hey, are you here for the Disney Trainers Program? You're in the wrong room! Come over here." He led us to a different room which was set up perfectly. We were greeted with a warm handshake and a smile. Music was playing. Coffee was ready. A welcome sign was on the door. Everything was in place. We gave a huge sigh of relief! Of course, the two rooms were set up to show us the powerful difference.

Many trainers fall into the captured prisoner syndrome, which is "I don't need to be good, they *have* to be here. You're swimming in my lane so I'll say what I want and do what I want. You're not my guest, you're an employee, just like me."

Everyone Must Attend Orientation

An important part of the Disney Difference is that everyone must complete this new employee orientation before starting to work at Walt Disney World. Unfortunately, I see other companies sometimes cheat on this process. They initially say, "Give me a body, any body to answer phones over here at the employment center…I can't wait for them to go through training." And then they say, "What did you send me? This new person doesn't know anything…and they're not very nice to our customers." And the cycle continues.

A huge commitment for organizations is when they say, "We're not going to let just anyone serve our customers until they have been effectively trained in our way of doing business." Many decades ago, Disney said, "We're not going to let just anyone serve our guests until they know the Disney Way of doing business." If you let a new employee start working for one to three weeks before going to the new employee orientation training session, what unintended consequences might have happened to them, or worse, to those they served before they learned the company way of doing things?

At Disney, everyone attends Disney Traditions on day one. Everyone…no matter their experience, education, job title, or authority.

I remember a CEO coming to the Disney Institute (the corporate training arm of the Disney company) and learning how extensive the training was for every single employee. He asked, "What if we spend all of that time training them, and they leave?"

My reply was, "What if you don't train them…and they stay?"

Redesigning your orientation will help lay the foundation for success so that every new employee is inspired and committed to work for your organization.

35

Treat Employees Like VIPs

The idea at Disney is to treat every guest as a VIP — a very individual person — to make them feel special. For this to be sincere and authentic, it has to be modeled by how they treat each other. Cast members should feel the same level of individual treatment on day 1000 as they did on day one.

One of the ways you can make new employees in healthcare feel welcome is to offer a quick survey to discover the things they like. Armed with this information, you can make sure the employee break room is stocked with their favorite beverage or breakfast treat when they arrive.

Make Them Part of the Team on Day One

You can also take a tip from Disney and have a special name badge pre-ordered so your new employee will feel like part of the team on day one. Give them a tour of your facility on the first day so they know where to find the restrooms and break areas. It's also important to have their computer, clean workspace, and/or locker ready to go so they feel a sense of belonging and are set up for success on their first day.

Here's a story from one of our former clients that might provide some helpful ideas for you: We first created and developed baseball trading cards at Lehigh Valley Hospital because referring physicians would come to the hospital and no one would know who they were. On the trading card for each physician, there was a photo and personal information on the front and professional information on the back. The idea of baseball trading cards was then taken to the Rehabilitation Institute of Michigan, where their new employee orientation program is called "Training Camp" and has a sports theme. Each new employee receives a trading card which they can then hand out and share with others as an introduction.

Ultimately, it doesn't matter if you are onboarding a veteran physician, a new pharmacist, or a third shift transporter - people want to feel they've made a good decision about their new place of employment.

36

Treat Employees Exactly How You'd Like Them to Treat Patients

After working in healthcare for the past two decades, I see a big disconnect in patient centered organizations - sometimes, the employee mindset is: *If you're not my patient, then you're not my customer.*

A classic example is the hospital phone operator. If an employee dials "0" and gets the operator internally, you hear someone abruptly say, "Operator!" in a short, annoyed voice, as if your phone call is an interruption to their day. Yet, if you dial that same operator from a patient room or from an outside line you hear a delightful voice saying, "Good morning, thank you for calling General Hospital, this is Jodi, how may I help you?"

Why do operators treat those who are calling from the outside phone lines or patient rooms infinitely better than they treat their fellow care team members? Because in the minds of the operators:

1. *Patient first* means I'm here for patients, and everyone else is a bother.

2. We are not members of a "care team" - we are called staff, employees or associates.

3. We don't subscribe to the philosophy, "treat fellow employees exactly how you'd like them to treat patients."

At the Walt Disney World Resort, market research revealed four expectations Guests want from every Disney Cast Member, every time, always:

1. Make me feel special.

2. Treat me as an individual.

3. Treat me and my children with respect.

4. Have knowledgeable employees.

When Disney leaders shared these new guest expectations with Disney Cast Members, they said, if you want us to deliver that experience always, then what we (the Cast Members) need from you (our Leaders) is:

1. Make me feel special.

2. Treat me as an individual.

3. Treat me with respect.

4. Make me knowledgeable.

After that, Disney leaders worked with their fellow cast members to figure out how to make them feel special and treat them as an individual. One idea was to ask every new and existing cast member in your department to fill out a personal inventory sheet or "favorites" questionnaire. This questionnaire was totally voluntary, and it asked questions like:

1. What name shall we call you - first name, nickname or other? (special/individual)

2. What city and state are you from (or country)?

3. How do you like to be recognized (publicly or privately)?

4. Favorite snack food, soda, candy?

5. What do like to do on your day off?

After leaders received back this information, they were enabled to treat cast members as individuals - not just another employee or FTE (full time equivalent). It enabled leaders to personalize feedback, call them by the name they liked best and slip the perfect candy bar or movie tickets (best day off activity) into a thank you note. Most importantly, it modeled to the cast members exactly what they should do with visiting guests.

When this gets translated into healthcare, not only can you treat your healthcare team members specially, but they may come up with ways to mirror this on how they treat their patients.

You may have seen an **About Me Poster** in a healthcare setting. Imagine your grandfather can't speak, but you want the healthcare workers who care for him to know how special he is to you. These pre-made dry erase posters can be placed near the patient's bed to let employees know: the name he likes to be called, the people that are important to him, what he does or did for a living, his favorite form of music, the names of his pets, his favorite food, sports team, TV program, etc.

Imagine, an environmental services employee comes into your grandfather's ("RJ") room at 7:00 pm after having two days off and having never met your grandfather. Can she make him feel special and treat him with respect in less than 30 seconds? She can if she uses the "about me" poster!

She walks into Mr. Peterson's room, glances up at his board and says, "Good evening, RJ. My name is Jennifer and I'm here from housekeeping to help tidy up your room. Just blink twice of now is a good time for me to do that (blink, blink). I am sorry to see you are a New England Patriots fan, as I am originally from Buffalo, New York. GO BILLS! But considering the Patriots are in the NFL playoffs and the BILLS are not, I will cheer on your team this year...is that okay? (blink blink...big smile). I also see you like to watch Jeopardy. Would you like me to turn that on for you while I clean your room? (blink, blink, smile)."

All in less than 30 seconds and all designed to enable a human connection.

Prior to smart phones and the internet information explosion, Disney rolled out a number of information mechanisms that armed cast members with information that their guests needed, including:

1. Vital Information Boards - Information scrolling across digital display boards at all main cast member entrances displaying vital information for that day (operating hours, closures, weather, etc.)

2. Dial extension 4500 - Any time you need to know anything, a team of experts is there for you to help your guest.

3. Flash 4500 - A business memo handed to cast members by a security host as they clocked out or in for the day, updating them on vital information that just happened that day.

4. Tips Sheet - A small folded piece of paper carried by cast members in case any guest asks a question about any other theme park or activity on property. The tips sheet includes key phone numbers and information on the top 20 questions asked each day.

> *Healthcare leaders often forget their job is not to take care of the patient. Their job is to take care of those who take care of the patient.*

37

Allow Employees to Decompress and Recharge

Disney goes to great lengths to maintain a sense of magic in their theme parks, keeping a clear line between onstage and backstage. They also do an excellent job of providing cast members with backstage break areas (away from guests), as well as fully staffed cafeterias and places outside to relax and decompress during a busy shift. Guests at Disney theme parks don't see cast members in costume smoking a cigarette outside their work location, or taking their lunch break in a restaurant in the theme park along with paying guests. Why? Because it takes away from the magic.

Patients and visitors in hospitals and healthcare facilities are affected by things you might not necessarily want them to see.

Consider the stress level of employees at a hospital, urgent care, hospice, rehab, or other care facility. For nurses, opportunities to take breaks are often few and far between - often, they work two shifts back to back. When are they supposed to get some downtime? At the end of their second shift?

Employees need some space to call their own, to decompress, de-stress, and relax, if only for a few minutes. It doesn't have to be anything fancy, but a break room or lounge away from patients and away from the activity of the facility will provide employees with a much-needed time out.

Consider how you might feel if you saw your father's heart surgeon eating lunch, texting, or taking a nap? Of course the surgeon needs to eat, sleep, and relax, but how might this affect your *perception* of the surgeon?

At one healthcare system we visited, employees in white coats stand on a public sidewalk and take a smoke break, right next to a Cancer Center sign. They do this because of a lack of backstage areas for team members, but how do you think it makes patients or visitors feel when they witness it?

We must give employees a time and a place to decompress backstage or we risk having them decompress onstage.

38

Think "Onstage"

Disney cast members work while others play, and they never cross the line. For instance, many celebrities visit the Disney parks and cast members are not permitted to ask for a photo or autograph. Why? Because that crosses a line – the celebrity is at play, and the cast members are at work.

Where do you Draw the Line?

Does healthcare have a line? Many healthcare workers wear their uniforms to the supermarket. They may be off the clock, but aren't they still representing their organization while in uniform?

When I was working at Walt Disney World, I knew of a young woman who stood up from her table at a lounge on Disney property and said very loudly, "I'm drunk and I have to play Mary Poppins tomorrow!" A Disney leader overheard this and said, "Don't worry. You don't have to go to work tomorrow. Or any day after that. You no longer have a job." The truth is, a cast member who is off the clock is still representing the Disney brand and must preserve the Disney magic.

There are many positive examples of this, too. What was astonishing to me was that at least once per week during the 20 years I worked for Disney, I would see a cast member with their car pulled over on the side of the road to help a guest who was lost. At Disney, you are always onstage and always representing your organization, whether you are at work or not.

What is the healthcare worker's responsibility to their employer's brand when they are off the clock, in the community, or on social media? Remember that in reality - perception is defined by the person who does the perceiving.

Perception is defined by the person who does the perceiving.

39

Train Your Vendors, Contractors and Volunteers

At Disney, everyone begins with the same level of training. For limited English speaking new cast members, training is provided in Spanish, Creole, and Haitian. The same nuts and bolts instruction for frontline leaders and staff is also provided for contracted workers. They wear a Disney name tag, so the expectation is that they will act like a Disney cast member.

One of the ways healthcare falls short in delivering a consistent patient experience is that all workers are not treated equally. In other words, not every person involved in the patient experience goes through the same level of training. For example, most physician orientations consist of a 45-minute conversation with the Chief Medical Officer. Many housekeeping contractors do their own onboarding and training, as do the food service contractors. The radiology technology orientation is all about the clinic's practices and scheduling. And volunteers do their own thing.

Contracts written for outsourced services like physician groups (including emergency department, surgical, hospitalists, and anesthesiologists), valet parking, food service, and housekeeping typically don't have a customer service accountability component as part of their contracts, nor do they have a mandatory training component.

The challenge is that most hospitals and care organizations don't fully train contracted employees, vendors, and volunteers – yet when it comes to the patient experience, the front line drives the bottom line. Take a moment to think about who gets the valet parking contract? Typically, it's the lowest cost provider, and you get what you pay for.

Make sure your culture is explicitly articulated in your vendor contracts. Provide clear expectations on what you do and do not stand for. All employees, contractors, vendors, and volunteers should go through the same or similar on-boarding, including on-the-job training. Everyone, including volunteers, must be held accountable for their work performance.

Understand the Customer's Perspective: "Through the Patient's Eyes"

"The golden rule is to treat others the way you would like to be treated. Even better is *The Platinum Rule*, which is to treat others the way <u>they</u> wish to be treated. The challenge becomes finding out what they want."

- Jake Poore

40

Do Little Things to Make a Big Difference

Would it surprise you to learn that the bandages at Disney theme park first aid stations have Mickey, Minnie, and other Disney characters printed right on them? It just makes sense, right? Oh sure, it's great marketing, but consider a boo-boo or skinned knee from a tearful child's point of view. Seeing their favorite character on a bandage is a small but kind way to bring a smile and stop the tears.

If you're required to use the plain bandages rather than the pre-printed, specially-themed ones, you can still make a little magic. My wife recently brought our kids for a routine blood draw. When the nurse was finished with each child, she put a bandage over the area and then used a permanent marker pen to draw smiley faces on each one! It didn't cost any extra time or money, but it sure made our kids smile.

A recent study shows that people react to smiley faces (and other emojis) in exactly the same way as they react to an actual human smile…so a little smiley face on a bandage can have a huge impact!

Here are a few examples of "little things" from in and out of healthcare to get your creative juices flowing:

- In many restaurants, the servers put smiley faces on checks and bring your take-out food wrapped in foil in the shape of a swan.

- A pediatrician wears a Mickey Mouse watch to seem more approachable and relatable to his patients.

- A cashier sees the customer's hands are full and so she turns the credit card receipt around and holds it for the customer to sign their name. (How many cash registers do you have in your hospital? Probably a minimum of five, right? Pharmacy, gift shop, cafeteria, admissions, emergency room, etc.)

One final thought on little things making a big difference: Disney has a class for their merchandise cast members called "Merchantainment," in which they teach cast members how to proactively put a little magic into every transaction. For example, cashiers are taught a few common phrases in several different languages so the cast member can build a bridge and extend a greeting in the guest's language. If your hospital or care facility is in an area where multiple languages are common, it may make sense to hire employees who speak multiple languages. At the very least, consider arming your employees with a few key phrases to help bridge the communication gap.

41

Treat Every Patient As a VIP

Patients in healthcare don't want to be identified by their illness. No one I know wants to be called "the hip in room 103." And why would they? Nurses and doctors have all your vital information on the hospital computer and on the dry erase board, right?

When people are on vacation at Walt Disney World they don't want to be treated as faceless numbers in a crowd. People like to be treated uniquely, as individuals. Most of them saved for quite some time to afford the trip, and they expect to be treated to Disney's world-class service. Cast members may not know who you are or where you're from, but they still go the extra mile to treat you like a VIP - a very individual person.

Years ago, I accompanied a doctor on his rounds. As we were ending a visit in an elderly woman's room, I asked her, "Ma'am, is there anything we can do here to make your stay more enjoyable?" She smiled and hesitated at first, and then said, "Well…it IS my birthday. I'm 100 years old today, and if it's not too much trouble, could I get a piece of birthday cake?"

I was shocked! How did the care team not know it was this woman's birthday, let alone her 100th? Although the information was on the patient's medical chart, it had simply been overlooked. After checking with her doctor and the dietician, we had a piece of cake delivered to this woman, complete with balloons and streamers, and she celebrated her milestone birthday with a smile.

Dr. Jesse Kramer at Mercy Medical Group in California has a great example of how he and his team make people feel like VIPs. It all starts with the medical assistants and nurses who carefully gather vital information, which includes more than just the patient's weight and vital signs. In addition to the expected data, they also make note of any personal information or milestones the patient mentions. In the instance I observed, a patient casually mentioned that she just visited her grandson who was home from college. She was proud that he was offered a full scholarship to play baseball at a state school. As the Medical Assistant measured the patient's vitals, she also wrote this information down on the back of the patient charge sheet, securing it to the clipboard so the doctor would see it prior to visiting the patient. The doctor quickly read the "patient's vitals" and then congratulated her on her son's college acceptance.

The care team set the doctor up for success – but it doesn't end there. These notes are stored in the patient record so when the patient returns a year later and the doctor asks how her grandson is doing in his first year of college, the patient's jaw drops as she thinks, "How could he possibly have remembered?!"

In healthcare, the challenge is to adapt VIP treatment to the work environment and remember that everyone is a VIP - a very individual person.

42

Go Undercover

Empathy is difficult to teach. It is best experienced first-hand. The most empathetic caregivers are typically the ones who have gone through similar experiences themselves.

One of the main reasons people call Disney the happiest place on earth is because Disney has knowledgeable, friendly employees. One of the ways they do this is by encouraging their cast members to visit the theme parks on their days off - for free! They also give cast members a handful of passes to share so they can enjoy the theme parks with their family a few times a year.

While free tickets are a great perk for Disney cast members, they really serve a greater purpose.

When employees become park guests, they can see and feel what their guests experience, including overhearing guest complaints while waiting in line. They hear comments that often don't make it to the Guest Relations (customer service) cast members at the front of the parks. This experience helps to build empathy when dealing with guest situations, and it can inspire cast members to come up with ways to improve the guest experience.

Visiting the parks as a guest allows cast members to become experts at way-finding, which can be a big problem in healthcare. If you ask someone how to get somewhere in a hospital or care facility, it surprises me how many people have no idea and simply respond by saying, "I don't know, I've never been there." Patients want directions, but what they need is a human GPS to take them there.

As part of new employee orientation at the Rehabilitation Institute of Michigan, employees participate in a scavenger hunt while using a wheelchair. They do this in order to gain experience in what it's like to navigate the patient experience.

In some hospitals, employees also get a voucher to stay in a patient bed overnight, with the door open, and a requirement to eat the food.

There are lots of ways to "flip the lens" and see things through the patient's eyes.   As leaders, you should play the role of "undercover boss" and walk your areas making mental notes. Or, you could even ride a gurney! Have a team member push you along and experience what the patient sees, hears, and smells. Solid white walls? Emergency alarms? Water stained ceiling tiles? How scary is it? What could you do to make that experience better for the next patient?

43

Drive Rapid Feedback for Rapid Response

One of the great challenges in healthcare is a lack of timeliness around patient feedback. Many patient satisfaction surveys are not administered until a week or more *after* a patient's departure, and they're not always returned in a timely manner, making the data old and irrelevant. In addition, the sample size is usually so small that most physicians consider it to be statistically insignificant. This is a great source of frustration for hospital administrators and performance excellence teams.

Physicians are scientists. Many physicians will challenge the validity of their patient satisfaction scores based upon the number of surveys returned. A sufficient quantity needs to be returned to make the data statistically significant. Therefore, before actual patient satisfaction scores can have an impact on your medical staff, you will want to increase the response rate. Your attention should be spent on incentivizing providers to encourage their patients to take the time to fill out the survey (and thereby raise the response rate) instead of on the actual results.

Discharge phone calls were institutionalized about ten years ago, with the premise being that the provider's office would call the patient at home within 24-48 hours of departure. What a wonderful common sense idea! It started out as a way to verify clinical compliance and turned into a way to make dissatisfied patients a bit happier. This, in turn, could positively influence scores on the patient satisfaction survey. But most of these mechanisms or listening posts are much too late! The patient had already left the building. And they've already posted about their bad experience on Facebook, LinkedIn, Twitter, and Yelp for everyone to read.

For decades at the Walt Disney Company, we used a low-tech way to get rapid feedback: exit interviews. As people were leaving the parks or checking out of hotels, we would get immediate feedback on a few quick questions. It was a great way to fix a mistake, to give an employee or department immediate feedback for exceptional behavior, and get a sampling size or pulse of people that day.

When the University of Chicago opened their Center for Advanced Medicine, they adopted a similar type of mechanism. They called it rapid feedback, rapid response. They handed a survey to people when they arrived and collected it before they left. Patients would tell what they loved about the process and what they didn't. It was a safe, easy way to get immediate feedback and also could be turned in anonymously. The key is immediate action. If the patient put their name on the form they would get a call that night, allowing for immediate feedback to providers and staff.

Baystate Health in Massachusetts does it with smiley/automated response machines, positioned at exit doors, and they have a 99% response rate, which is statistically significant. They encourage you to respond regardless of how they think you'll score them.

44

Remember Celebrations

Whether it's your birthday, anniversary, honeymoon, or your very first visit, Disney has a special pin just for you. Throughout your visit, cast members who see your pin will come up to you and join in your celebration by singing Happy Birthday or wishing you a Happy Anniversary. It's a simple way to bring a little extra magic to guests.

When our daughter dressed up as Cinderella and we went to the Magic Kingdom, everyone called her "Princess" or "Your Highness," bowing and curtsying to her along the way. To her, it felt special and magical.

Kids needs don't change when they go to hospitals. Positively distracting them or allowing them to pretend to be a mythical or magical character can work wonders for their spirits or to reduce anxiety. It elevates the experience to a whole new level; it elevates beyond the sickness.

You can also remember special occasions for employees.

We begin every one of our team meetings by asking if anyone has any celebrations or good news to share. Some of our team members are parents, so often they'll mention the first day of school or school award. Others may mention a new pet, special family visit, or a favorite sports team's win. It's a great way to enter on the human and it helps to foster teamwork, camaraderie, and unity among our group.

45

Celebrate Achievements Big and Small

At Disney, buttons are used to celebrate life's important accomplishments, such as birthdays or anniversaries. However, they are also used to celebrate just about anything that a guest believes is worth celebrating. This is accomplished by a button that says "I'm Celebrating!" and then space and a marker for the wearer to fill in what he or she is celebrating.

At National Rehabilitation Hospital in Washington D.C., they call their celebrations "little victories." The goal today is to sit up. Congratulations, that's a victory! The goal today is to eat solid food. Congratulations! That's another victory. These are all little victories in rehabilitation. They even have a six foot whimsical character named Vic that celebrates all these little victories. Vic rounds on patients and hands out "little Vics" (tiny little Vic stuffed animals).

Even though receiving medical care is often uncomfortable and, many times, accompanied by a fear of the unknown, it's also full of achievements, and even sometimes life celebrations. Yet surprisingly, healthcare often does not plan for these moments in life. In a healthcare setting, different kinds of achievements for both employees and patients can, and should, be celebrated.

46

Create an Online Welcome Video

Whether you're planning a stay at a Disney resort hotel, Disney cruise, or Disney timeshare, or even planning a wedding for your daughter, Disney can send you videos to help plan and set expectations for it all.

- A nervous grandfather will soon have his second knee replacement operation.

- A scared teenager is being admitted for her first open-heart surgery.

- A young mother is receiving a kidney transplant.

What will their upcoming hospital stay be like? What can they expect?

Patients are scared. Our job is to help reduce that fear and anxiety in any way we can. One way to proactively address these fears is by offering a "Welcome Video" on your website.

Kaiser Permanente, Cancer Treatment Centers of America, and many others have produced a "Welcome" video for their patients to watch before they're admitted. Your video can feature pictures of the hospital and patient rooms as well as some members of the care team. What about a virtual tour of the hospital? Or better yet, a guided, step-by-step tour of the admission process, beginning with where they should park and all the stops along the way.

Too high tech? You can also consider a written checklist with step-by-step instructions, individualized by need, that can be downloaded from your website. I got one when I turned 50 and had to get my first colonoscopy. It was very helpful.

A welcome video or guided instructions can be a great way to share the mission and service promise of your hospital or organization in a way that patients can see, hear, and understand. And it can explain the kind of care patients can expect before, during and after their stay and throughout their healing process.

47

We've Been Expecting You

I visited a facility where one of the patients, Mr. Klausen, shared a common healthcare frustration with me. For ten straight days he arrived at the hospital for wound therapy.

- For ten straight days, the valet asked if he'd like his car to be valet parked.

- For ten straight days, security told him he couldn't go up in the elevator until 7:00 AM.

- For ten straight days, the receptionist didn't greet him, but told him to sign in.

- For ten straight days, he was weighed in the hallway on the way to the exam room with no explanation as to why.

Mr. Klausen asked me, "Am I that forgettable that for ten straight days, no one remembers me?"

With tens of thousands of resort guests visiting Walt Disney World each year it's impossible to remember each and every guest. But here's one hospitality strategy Disney uses: if you go to Disney's Yacht & Beach Club Resort, you first pass through a security gate. The security cast member says, "Hi. Welcome to Disney's Yacht & Beach

Club Resort. Is this your first time staying with us?" If it's not, you're greeted with a hearty, "Welcome back!" Then the security guard radios ahead to the valet parker, who can then greet you with "Welcome back, Mr. Poore, we've been expecting you!"

That cast member will signal the next cast member, typically a bellman, to indicate that you are a return guest, and often includes your name. A similar process is repeated down the line so that every subsequent cast member can say, "Welcome back, Mr. Poore!" The result is you feel like a **valued guest.**

Disney also puts a parking pass in your windshield and writes your last name on it. So even if they're not able to call ahead, the valet can still address you by your name and welcome you back. The valet can then seamlessly hand you over to the bellman, "Let me get Bob to help you with your luggage. Bob, this is Mr. Poore."

In a hospital, it works well when the valet writes your name on all three valet tickets: your ticket, the ticket that attaches to the keys, and the ticket that goes onto your dashboard. "Mr. Poore, you're going to oncology today for your treatment? When you finish with your treatment, hand your ticket to the receptionist on the floor so we can pull your car around." When you hand your ticket to the receptionist, she can then use your name and say, "Mr. Poore, I'll call to have your car brought up for you."

Another way to adapt this concept in healthcare is to greet each person who signs in with, "Good morning, Mr. Poore, we've been expecting you." We could put a star next to the name of anyone who has been before, signaling to others on the team to say, "Welcome back!"

We could also enhance technology to allow for patient photos to be included in electronic medical records so that when a patient arrives, she can be recognized and greeted with a warm, "Good morning, Mrs. Jones, we've been expecting you!"

Service Behaviors

"I've learned that people will forget what you said,
people will forget what you did,
but people will never forget
how you made them feel."

- Maya Angelou

48

Go the Extra Mile

Going the extra mile can have a huge impact on improving the patient experience. To start, consider encouraging the front reception desk team to create a system to make things more patient-friendly and warmer.

For example, in many primary care clinics and surgery waiting areas in hospitals, the standard operation is for a medical assistant to stand by the door of the waiting area and shout your name out to the entire group of people waiting.

When my wife goes to the doctor for a scheduled appointment, and she is the only female waiting in the room, why does the medical assistant stand with a hand on the back office door and just yell out her name? Because they have always done it that way. That is how the assistant was trained and that's how she will train others, until someone asks the patient, "Is that what you want?"

If Disney ran the waiting area at this office, the medical assistant would walk right up to my wife and say, "Mrs. Poore, we're ready to take you back now." Even if there were many women in the waiting area, they would know which one is Mrs. Poore. How does Disney do it? Simple. When a patient checks in, the receptionist writes down unique clothing identifiers to distinguish that patient from others in the reception area. They might even use quotes to communicate the name the patient prefers to be called.

If patient "Bob Jones" is wearing a blue shirt and has a white beard, the front desk team can make a small note on the patient folder. Then, the medical assistant can read that note and easily walk directly to the patient to invite him back to the clinical area. This is certainly friendlier and kinder than shouting 'MR. JONES. MR. ROBERT JONES!' from the door.

Why is it called going the extra mile? The average clinic sees about 30-50 patients per day. By walking an extra 30 feet over to each patient and by greeting them quietly and personally, the patient will feel like a VIP, but also if you add up all the patients you see that week, you will likely walk an extra mile! (or 5,280 feet).

49

Knock... And Wait for a Response

Remember the last time you stayed at a Disney hotel, or any hotel for that matter, and the housekeeper barged in on you while you were still sleeping?

Of course you don't!

Why? Because, although the housekeeping staff has master keys to every room, they would never dream of entering a room without first knocking and waiting for a reply. Why not? Because it's your room. And it's your hard-earned money paying for that room.

So why then do we still do this to patients in hospitals? Aren't they the same people who stay in hotels? I know they're sick, but shouldn't they be treated with the same dignity and respect as people who stay in hotels?

It just takes an extra second or two, but knocking before entering a patient's room is a common courtesy. The second part of this process is to wait for permission to enter the room after knocking. It's easy to knock and then just barge in, but knocking and then waiting for permission to enter shows respect. It also preserves the patient's dignity by avoiding any potentially embarrassing situations for the patient.

People don't change from when they stay in a hotel to when they stay in a hospital. They are the same people. People's expectations of their hard-earned cash don't change when they leave a hotel room and are now in a hospital room. Consumerism has arrived. Now that consumer awareness is here in healthcare, patients are paying more out of pocket costs and scrutinizing the bill. "You charged me $1,200 for the hospital room for a night? I have never paid $1,200 for a hotel room! And the door was open all night so I didn't even get any sleep!"

Hospital staff often think of the rooms as being *theirs*. I've seen too many caregivers knock and then walk right in as if they owned the place. We would never walk into someone's hotel room without permission, and it makes sense to show the same courtesy to our patients.

Of course there are exceptions. Hospital staff need to enter patient rooms 24/7, and you certainly don't want to wake up a patient who just fell asleep if it can be avoided. Similarly, some patients are not physically able to verbally respond to your knock. Deal with the exceptions as needed without jeopardizing the patient's right to privacy.

50

Make Eye Contact and Smile

I'm here to save your butt, not kiss it.

Whether that phrase is a mantra or just legend doesn't really matter. Many healthcare workers feel they don't have time to be nice because they're too busy saving lives and doing their actual job tasks.

Research has shown that being nice is an incredibly important catalyst to the healing experience. We have to do the little things that connect patient care to patient understanding, because if we don't, then patients may not like us. And if they don't like us, then they may not trust us, and trust is a vital component of getting patients to adhere to their care plan. It takes only seconds to build trust or erode it.

Much of my career at Disney was spent trying to operationalize friendliness and uphold our reputation as the friendliest place on earth. Getting 74,000 cast members to smile is no easy task. One place to start is to help cast members understand why a smile is so important. Disney knows that when you smile at a visitor or guest, it makes you approachable. When you make eye contact or get to someone's eye level, like a three foot tall child or a grandmother in a wheelchair, it shows respect. This makes an immediate connection and builds trust. When a family interacts with between 60-70 cast members every day of their vacation, a lot of connections are made and trust is built. This trust helps to uphold Disney's reputation as the friendliest place on Earth.

When someone makes eye contact with you, but isn't smiling, it can feel awkward. That's why we recommend making eye contact _and_ smiling at the same time. This might seem kind of obvious, but with our use of electronic devices and monitors, sometimes we become so busy looking at data on a screen that we forget to engage with a patient by looking at them.

My wife and I were in a hospital room when a caregiver came in and immediately proceeded to ask questions while staring at and typing into a computer. She never once looked up at my wife, who was in labor and mere hours from giving birth!

Caregivers often keep their eyes down as they walk along the halls instead of looking up, making eye contact, and smiling at the people they pass by. Typically, health care workers tell us they don't want to be stopped because they have so much to do. But how much time do you think is lost by missing that human connection, and then how much is gained when patients see staff smiling at them as they pass?

When I coach people about making eye contact and smiling, I remind them that you get one point if you smile OR make eye contact, but you get FIVE points (in the eyes of the patient) if you do both. It makes a positive difference to patients and visitors when you make eye contact with them **and** smile as you pass by.

51

Leverage Patient Trust Connectors

From the first day a new cast member starts at Disney, they learn how important body language is in every guest interaction. After making eye contact and smiling, they must continue to communicate nonverbally - through body language - that they are open and attentive.

Nonverbal cues are everywhere, not just in the world of healthcare. We often make snap decisions of others just based on their body language. How do you feel when you see someone with their head propped up in their hands, or their arms crossed, or their hands on their hips? How about if they're clicking a pen nonstop, or drumming their fingers on a table, or tapping their foot? What signals do these send? These are just some examples of how we nonverbally communicate to others that we don't care about them or what they're saying or feeling. This erodes trust.

When I taught the First Impressions team (valet parking, security, front desk, and volunteers) at Lehigh Valley Hospital, we created a phrase to help enable warm welcomes and fond farewells. We called it stop, drop and greet. As long as safety is not being jeopardized, stop what you're doing, drop what you're doing, and greet the person. The best way to stop, drop and greet is with eye contact, a smile, and by adjusting your body so that you're facing the person in an open and welcoming manner. All three are patient trust connectors: **eye contact**, a **smile** and **body language**.

If the person you're speaking with is traveling in a wheelchair or is a small child, take a knee and adjust your body so you're both at **eye level**. If possible, sit down, but if you're standing, be sure to **uncross your arms**. Crossed arms are a nonverbal cue to the patient or guest that you might be angry or unavailable.

While talking with a patient, focus on them and not the patient record or a computer screen. Not looking at the patient tells the patient that you're distracted or unsympathetic to their concerns.

Remember, when you're standing over a patient who is in a wheelchair or a bed, the effect is that you "look down your nose at them." When you are talking over your shoulder to someone while you are facing a computer on wheels, you're giving someone the "cold shoulder." These are the unintended consequences of not being intentional.

Use open and intentional nonverbal behaviors for more successful interpersonal communication. They're a great way to build trust and to show others that your attention is focused completely on them.

52

Adjust Your Altitude

Healthcare professionals are constantly playing beat the clock while trying to attend to every patient on a planned or responsive schedule. And while we can't add any more hours to the day, there is something we can do to build trust with patients that takes little to no time. We can adjust our **altitude**.

A study performed at the University of Kansas Hospital shows that patients whose doctors sit with them, versus standing, *perceive* that the doctor spent 40% longer with them than they actually did.[1] A second study, published in the *PEC Journal Online*, states that:

> Simply sitting instead of standing at a patient's bedside can have a significant impact on patient satisfaction, patient compliance, and provider–patient rapport, all of which are known factors in decreased litigation, decreased lengths of stay, decreased costs, and improved clinical outcomes.[2]

The first study illustrates an interesting point. A provider who sits can spend less time in the room while seeming to spend more time in the patient's eyes.

A patient's perception of their care changes depending on if they (or you) are standing, sitting or lying down. Whether you're going out to get an elderly woman in the waiting room, speaking to someone in a wheelchair, or about to examine someone in a patient bed, try your best to get to their eye level and make eye contact. Appropriateness is learned by trial and error. Practice this to find out what works best for you and your team.

Take special care when talking to children by taking a moment to physically adjust your altitude to their level. No matter how tall you are, your presence can be intimidating to a person of any age. Add in a white coat, stethoscope, or other medical supplies, and you could easily frighten patients. Try to get down to their eye level. Talk in a soft, reassuring voice. Be honest and speak directly to them as well as their family members. People will appreciate your efforts and they will begin to trust you.

Watch Snow White when she is talking to a child at a Disney park. She gracefully bends down to the child's eye level to greet the child and sign an autograph. I've even seen Pluto crouch down for a photograph with a small child. This is something that Disney characters are taught, and they practice, always.

53

Introduce Yourself and Your Role

At Walt Disney World, frontline cast members wear costumes that fit their role and a clearly printed name tag, making it easy for guests to know the cast members' names and roles. But not all cast members are in costume. Cast members in street clothes wear a name tag and identification badge, but will always make a concerted effort to introduce themselves to a guest and explain their role with the company. "Hello Mr. Poore. I'm Elonzo, the front desk manager here at Disney's Port Orleans Resort. How may I assist you?"

Introductions and greetings are common at most restaurants. After being seated you'll soon be greeted with, "Hi, my name is John, and I will be your server this evening. Have you been here before?"

What happens in a healthcare setting? After knocking and waiting for a response before entering a room, caregivers should also be sure to introduce themselves so the patient knows **who** is there and **what** they will be doing in the room. This is especially helpful if your name tag is hard to read.

Be sure to introduce your role in a language patients and their family members can understand. For example, instead of saying, "Hi, I'm Jake, and I'm from PT," try, "Hi, I'm Jake, and I am your Physical Therapist. Your doctor has ordered for you to walk in the hallway, and I'm here to walk with you." Explain terms like PT, RN, PA, hospitalist, etc.

There are many unintended ways we erode trust and create anxiety for patients. Introducing ourselves helps to build trust and connect with patients. It takes no extra time, and although it might sound simple and small, it can make a world of difference.

54

Discover Your Patient's Preferred Name

Years ago, a family visited the Magic Kingdom with their two young daughters. It was a busy day and they waited in a long line to meet their favorite princess, Snow White. When they finally got to the front of the line, they told Snow White their names, took some pictures and even got her autograph. The daughters were sad to have the visit end, but were happy to have met Snow White. Hours later, during the three o'clock parade, the girls spotted Snow White on one of the parade floats. To their amazement, Snow White saw them – and she called them by name! Thousands of people visit the Magic Kingdom everyday and yet Snow White remembered *their names.* The girls were in heaven!

To the patient, the sound of their own name is music to their ears! And we don't mean the name on their medical record, although that may be suitable. Don't assume that the name on the medical record is the name the patient prefers to be called. That's their formal, legal name. It may not always be their personal preference (Even my friends don't know that my legal name is Eric since I always go by Jake!).

So how will you know what name to use? Just ask them! And then after you ask them, **use it.** Write it in a highly visible space (on a white board, in the electronic medical record, in patient notes, etc.), so that everyone on the healthcare team sees it and uses it.

As we've mentioned many times in other lessons, leaders in healthcare have to get everyone to understand they have a role on the care team. The name of the patient and their family members are not just for nurses and doctors, they're also important for housekeeping, transporters, security officers and volunteers.

Many people do not have access to the electronic medical records. Since the introduction of the HIPAA law, we have been very reluctant to put the patient's name on the outside of the door out of concern for their privacy and confidentiality. However, what does the patient want? Maybe we could ask kids at a children's hospital what name they'd like put on their door so we can all call him or her by that name.

At one children's hospital I visited, kids were allowed to decorate a poster for the door of their hospital room, complete with pictures and the name they wanted to be called. My own son Logan might call himself Super-Logan and put up pictures of Minecraft, his favorite game.

55

Walk with Patients
and Families

You can't walk through a Disney theme park without passing hundreds of guests with their eyes glued to a printed map of the park. Which way is the Jungle Cruise? Where is Mickey Mouse? Where are the restrooms?

One of my favorite things to do as a leader at Disney was to help guests navigate the parks. Oftentimes, that meant literally walking with guests, but most times it involved getting really familiar with the park guide maps. We wouldn't just tell guests where all the popular rides were and then point the way. We showed them. We gave them visual and verbal cues to remember. We plotted out every turn and we highlighted it on their map so they had a reference. We walked them there whenever possible and shared the best kept secrets along the way.

We can do the same in healthcare. Instead of ending an exam or a consultation in the exam room, why not walk the patient to the front reception or check-out desk? As you walk, you can repeat any instructions and ask if they have any questions or concerns. This may sound simple and insignificant, but patients don't know your office or your hospital as well as you do. Walking the patient out is a great opportunity to end the visit with a human touch.

Wanting to increase his patient satisfaction scores, a neurologist at Dignity Health Medical Foundation, asked me to find out why one of his colleagues had better patient satisfaction scores than he did. Come to find out, his colleague did something unique. After a typical exam, he would physically walk his patient to the front desk, ending the appointment on the human side. He originally did it for efficiency purposes so his medical assistant could clean the exam room faster and prepare the next patient, but what he found out was it had many other benefits:

1. Better communication with the front desk team regarding followup appointments.

2. An opportunity to answer any last minute questions for patients, which stopped subsequent interruptions.

3. Patients loved the good-bye handshake or hug.

4. Other patients and visitors in the waiting lounge appreciated seeing the human touch.

Create a Caring Language

"In healthcare, our goal is to create a connection
with patients and build a relationship of trust.
But when we use jargon, acronyms, and internal
company-speak, we unintentionally erode trust."

- Jake Poore

56

Speak in a Language They Can Understand

When we speak in our industry language and not in a common language that our customers can understand, it can sometimes have unintended consequences.

When my son was five years-old, he fell off the top of the slide in our backyard and fractured his elbow. My wife and I scooped him up and drove him to the local hospital, where we waited 38 minutes in the emergency room until a nurse finally came out to get us. She walked right up to my wife and said, "We are ready to triage your son now." My wife then looked at me with big wide open eyes, and I asked, "Why are you looking at me?" She said, "Well, you took three years of French, what in the world does triage mean?!" So you see, sometimes at the very first step of the healthcare journey, and also at the very last step, we can add anxiety and confusion just by using terms that patients don't fully understand.

If we really want to become a patient-driven organization, we need to be intentional about the words and phrases we use, so that we make connections with patients and not just speak at them.

Are we using phrases and industry-speak because we've always done it that way? Acronyms and jargon are internal communication shortcuts. They are "me-first," not "patient-first."

Rewind back to my very first days at Disney when they warned me about this: Don't use acronyms and industry jargon; you may inadvertently confuse our guests, or worse, ruin their vacation.

Make no mistake...cast members are full of jargon. "HOP is 101 so let's allow our cast to ER or deploy to DAK instead." What?? "The Hall of Presidents (HOP) is not working right now (101) so let's allow our employees (cast) to have an early release (ER) or go over (deploy) to Disney's Animal Kingdom (DAK) instead."

Every company has jargon for their employees...but it's NOT something they should use with their patients.

(See Lesson #2 for additional examples.)

57

Use Human-Business-Human®

One of our core philosophies at Integrated Loyalty Systems is Human - Business - Human® (HBH). It's a simple and easy process to remember. Here's how it works:

- Begin every patient and employee interaction with something **human** - a friendly greeting and smile.

- Move to the **clinical or business** tasks at hand.

- End the interaction with another **human** element.

Think about checking in to a hotel. You wait in line and the first word you hear is, "Next!" *Straight to business.* No human touch at all. Wouldn't it be better if the attendant said, "Hi, who's next, please? Hello Mr. Smith, welcome to the Chicago Hilton. Is this your first visit to the windy city?"

What does **"enter on the human"** look like in healthcare? Well, the more we enter on the human and talk with patients about the non-medical aspects of their lives, the higher the patient satisfaction ratings we earn.

People crave personal attention. If you're not sure where to start, begin with their name. This is especially true for women who are also mothers. They're addressed as "Mom" so frequently that they rarely hear their given name! By setting the tone with a warm welcome and entering on the human, you can then switch gears to the procedural or clinical reason for the visit as your patient becomes less anxious and more at ease.

When we conduct our "mystery shopper" analysis in hospitals, the very first place the 'human' gets lost is when we call the hospital operator, who usually answers by just stating the name of the hospital. No good morning. No hello. No offer to help. A very simple way to open with the human is to say "Good Morning! Thank you for choosing University Hospital, my name is Betty, how many I help you?" And before transferring the call, the operator can say, "My pleasure to connect you."

Begin each text or email *'on the human.'* Whether the email is professional or casual, find a way to begin or end with something personal.

Sending off a message to your team?

"Happy Monday, Team!" or "Great job on the XYZ project."

Then continue on with the purpose of the text or the email.

We enter on the human by making some kind of personal or human connection with the patient (or family member, employee or colleague). We conduct our business, and then we end on the human. How? By making another human connection.

For example: "Thanks for coming in today, Carol, and congratulations to you and Mike on your 20th wedding anniversary!" Or, "Good luck to your son this weekend in the Pinewood Derby!"

If you're following up with a new patient, you could say: "It was a pleasure meeting you. I hope you and your family enjoy your weekend."

In today's healthcare, there really is value to this humanistic approach. When we enter on the human, we create warm welcomes. When we create warm welcomes, we build a place where people feel cared for. When we exit on the human, we create fond farewells, where people feel valued and are more likely to return.

Think of our Human-Business-Human® approach as bookends on every conversation, including emails and phone calls. It's a way to begin and end your interaction with a simple, human touch and add a sense of personal connection to every patient and employee interaction.

58

Practice Caring Out Loud®

The average family will save for two to three years for a Disney vacation. It's an expensive place, and families have very high expectations for getting their money's worth. Because of these high expectations, it's imperative that they keep the guest in the loop every step of the way, especially when it comes to changes to normal protocol (closing of a swimming pool, canceling an Indiana Jones stunt show, attraction closed for refurbishment, etc.).

Caring Out Loud® means including the guest in the experience by narrating your processes out loud, or just 'keeping them in the loop' on what's coming next.

Many years ago, I was sitting in an airplane on the tarmac. We had taxied out to the runway when, without warning, the captain turned off the engine. He said nothing, so I feared engine problems or something worse. We eventually made it to our destination, but I worried about the engine the entire time.

Some time later, I flew another airline and the exact same situation occurred. This time, however, the captain announced, "Folks, it's a little busy at JFK today so I'm going to turn off the engine while we wait to conserve fuel. It might get a little bit hot in here, but I figured you'd rather that than us needing to go back to the terminal to refuel once it's finally our turn, which may take about 45 minutes. So please, take a nap and I'll let you know when they give us the go ahead." This second approach went a long way toward lowering anxiety and kept us involved as to why the decision was made to turn off the engine.

At Disney, they don't just tell people to get out of the pool without giving a reason. They care out loud by saying, "Folks we need you to please exit the pool now, as there is lightning in the area. Once it's passed, and it's safe, we'll be able to reopen the pool."

Caring Out Loud® can also answer a question, or anticipate customers' needs. For example, have you ever wondered how long that coffee in the waiting room has been sitting there? I always like to know if the coffee is fresh or if it's been sitting around all night. Do what Panera Bread does and place a chalkboard sign near the machine. Then, have an employee update the time whenever the coffee is freshly brewed.

In empty flower beds during the winter months, Disney will put up a sign that says, "Jack Frost paid us an unexpected visit." Or, you'll see a sign on a construction wall that says something like, "Please pardon our pixie dust as we create new, magical experiences for our guests."

How often is your hospital or care facility being renovated, updated, painted, or repaired? How do you communicate this to your patients, guests and employees? What option would you choose?

1. Say and do nothing.

2. Explain either verbally or by putting up a sign that says, "Construction underway."

3. Put up a sign that is "Disney-fied" that reads "Please pardon our dust as we expand our Radiology Department with new state-of-the-art equipment to improve our diagnostic capability."

59

Caring Out Loud® in Three Levels

At Disney University, I learned a very basic training mantra: *Tell them what you're gonna tell them. Then tell them. Then tell them what you told them.*

In healthcare, we've developed three levels of narrating your care out loud:

Level 1: Tell them what you're going to do (and why)

Level 2: Tell them what you're doing as you do it (narrate)

Level 3: Tell them what you did and the next step or person in the process (and build the next person up).

For example, here's how the three levels of Caring Out Loud® might look during a routine blood draw:

Tell them what you're gonna do: "Good morning Mr. Stevens. My name is Caroline from the lab, and I'm here to draw your blood. The doctor has ordered us to collect three vials of blood over the next 12 hours so we can monitor your blood sugar. Do you have any questions?"

Tell them what you're doing as you're doing it: "This tourniquet will pinch a little…this alcohol will feel a little cold…now a slight pinch…and we're done. This bandaid will seal the deal. We have a machine in the lab to measure the glucose in your blood, and we'll get that result to your doctor within the hour."

Tell them what you did and what the next steps in the process are: "Okay, Mr. Stevens, we're done with the first draw. My outstanding colleague, Anthony, be here in six hours to collect another vial. In the meantime, you can…."

What happens when we don't do this? In the absence of information, anxiety fills the void.

A few years ago, I brought my wife to the doctor when she was nine months pregnant. He started the exam, made a grunting noise and jotted something down. Then he continued with the exam. But he said nothing to us. My wife's eyes got really big. We were both very concerned that something was wrong. I asked the doctor, "Why did you make that grunting noise?" It turns out, he had remembered something from his previous patient that he needed to follow up with, and that's why he'd grunted and jotted himself a note. My wife and our baby were fine. But had we not asked, we would have gone home anxiously wondering what he **didn't** tell us.

---

*Caring Out Loud®
prevents unnecessary
anxiety and fear.*

60

Speaking in Code Can Help Preserve the Magic

Creating the happiest place on earth includes communicating with a cast of thousands who are spread out across a property the size of San Francisco. To make it easier, Walt Disney World cast members use a secret "inside" language of code words to help preserve the magic, especially when that magic is faced with the challenge of everyday life.

For example, if a guest becomes physically sick at the theme parks or resorts, cast members would never announce over a two-way radio: "Vomit cleanup in the main lobby!" Not only does this ruin the Disney magic, but it could also embarrass the sick guest as well as other guests that overhear that radio dispatch call.

Instead, Disney cast members might say, "I have a Code V in the main lobby." to discreetly notify the appropriate cast members to assist.

At a large hospital in the northeast, the CEO once asked me, "Jake, elevator etiquette is a challenge in this hospital. What's a dignified way to stop people from sharing personal, private, or inappropriate conversations with each other on the elevator or stop looking at their cell phones? How do we protect guests and visitors from hearing unpleasant communication among our employees?"

I told him that at Disney we used many radio codes for a variety of situations. Many were borrowed from the military or police sector and are primarily used when sending "cast only" radio messages. We also need to use appropriate codes that work for the hospital culture.

What employees need to know in this instance, and in every instance, is the difference between good show and bad show. Or, in healthcare terms, patient-first versus me-first.

I said to the CEO, "Jim, yesterday you told me you loved the old time comedians, Abbott and Costello, right? Well, what if you and I did a routine in our training workshop of their famous skit, Who's on First?, and we change it to be patient-first or me-first? The point of the skit is that this will now become our code. No guests will understand, but employees will. For example, if we observed two employees having an inappropriate conversation, we could simply say, "excuse me ladies, who's on first today?" (meaning – is your conversation being me-first or patient-first? Who is on first?)." The skit worked and the code became, "Who's on first?"

You probably already use a number of standard internal codes to help simplify or expedite communications, but you may want to consider making up some of your own internal code language. Use it to handle sensitive patient or visitor issues with extra care or to remind colleagues discreetly that a patient or family member is within earshot, such as in an elevator.

Anyone who regularly carries a hand-held two-way radio should consider wearing a wired ear piece at all times (like security and environmental services). This will assure private conversations stay private.

61

Elevate the Human Side of Business

The Disney company understands that even in our fast-paced, technologically advanced world, there is room for both the efficiency that technology brings, and the irreplaceable human touch.

The technology part is clear in the Disney phone app, the My Disney Experience website, Fast Pass+, and a host of innovative attractions. Ever since Walt Disney introduced the first fully synchronized sound cartoon (*Steamboat Willie*), the Disney company has recognized the need to stay ahead of the competition when it comes to making technological advances.

But what really sets Disney apart from the competition is the time and attention paid to the non-technical part of operating the number one entertainment company in the world: Disney understands the human side of entertainment and how to make emotional connections.

How much time does your healthcare organization spend on delivering the human side of healthcare? I know you are healing bodies, but are you also making emotional connections? Does your brand have a human side?

During an interview at the 2018 Forbes CMO Summit, President and Chief Customer Officer at Braze, Myles Kleeger, reported on research results from Forrester Research that showed people want to have human interaction in their business experiences. If a person perceives that the communication they are getting is coming from the human side, they are:

- 2.1 times more likely to love the company brand.

- 1.6 times more likely to feel satisfied with the company brand.

- 1.8 times more likely to recommend the brand to others.

In Lesson #57 I talked about the Human-Business-Human® approach from the perspective of compassion. The truth is, Human-Business-Human® has brand implications as well. In order to raise patient satisfaction and create loyalty, we must recognize that there is a business imperative to the human side of health care. Without it, we may achieve our clinical goals, but we'll fall short in delivering our vision and mission.

62

Preserve the Magic

At Disney, every cast member has an opportunity to play an important role in the Disney show by preserving the magic. For instance, any cast member walking through the theme park could be stopped and asked, "Excuse me, could you tell me where I can find a Mickey Mouse?" It seems like a pretty simple question, but one that takes some thoughtful response before being answered. One of Disney's core values is to "preserve the magic." There's **only one** Mickey Mouse. Cast members preserve the magic in the minds of their guests, and speak about Mickey like he's a real person.

For example, they might say, "You know, Mickey is a very busy guy, as he's the big cheese here. Let me check his schedule today." Or, "Mickey makes several appearances throughout the day — I'd be happy to check the show times to find out when and where he'll be next so you won't miss him."

Cast members never give the appearance that there is more than one Mickey. A bad way to respond to a guest's question would be, "Let me see where there's a Mickey scheduled today." For instance, if a guest asks why Mickey isn't out signing autographs, a cast member would NEVER say, "Because it's his lunch break," or "He's off the clock."

In healthcare, we need to preserve the magic of expertise. For instance, there are no bad doctors or dietitians or shifts or days of the week. There are no departments that are habitually late or behind. There's no sharing of rumors or innuendo with our guests. Questioning expertise *in front of patients* only creates more uncertainty, more fear, more anxiety, and more trepidation.

Once during an orthopedic hip surgery, an operating room technician was talking while the patient was still awake. This tech was complaining out loud about a piece of equipment that was going to be inserted into the patient's hip, and he remarked, "Ah, darn it. This thing never works right." This prompted the patient to ask, "Then why would you use it on my hip!?"

Never complain about a patient in front of a patient. Ever. A quick Google search of the patient who inadvertently recorded his surgical team with his smart phone will reveal a conversation I'm sure the care team wishes never happened.

Never bad-mouth or blame other staff or other departments in front of patients or their families. For example, a health care worker in the Emergency Room should never say, "I'm trying to get you a bed upstairs, but they're holding beds until the end of their shift." Or when the patient finally arrives on the medical floor, he or she shouldn't hear, "We would've gotten you here sooner but the ER sends us every Tom, Dick and Harry just to get rid of them." Or worse, "We're short-staffed today."

For suggestions to improve this, see Lesson #7: "Turn Handoffs Into Handovers."

63

Mind Your Manners

"Next!"

"What Do You Need?"

These phrases can be seen as abrupt and unfriendly, which is why you will never hear them uttered by Disney cast members. Disney trains their employees to be respectful and friendly when communicating with guests and also with each other.

Certainly, the enthusiasm you experience at Disney theme parks isn't the same thing as being in a hospital or healthcare facility. But in healthcare, you have the opportunity to make people feel loved, cared for, and respected by remembering one of the first things we're all taught as children: good manners. Why is saying please and thank you so often forgotten when we become adults?

The act of saying please or thank you shows respect and common courtesy. It can be a huge satisfier when used and a dissatisfier when not used, especially for older generations who really take notice.

Medical staff often feel like they are overworked and continually behind in their job tasks. They are not normally discourteous people, but they succumb to the pressures of the job. Don't fall into the trap of believing that "speed and efficiency is the enemy of courtesy and respect." They are not mutually exclusive.

A practice manager at one of our client's multiple medical offices sought to create warm welcomes and fond farewells at the front desk of the clinics she managed. Realizing that people remember their first and last impressions most, she observed clinic staff members to determine the frequency of hearing them say good-bye to their patients after an appointment or an exam.

She found that many front desk personnel finished the experience by saying, "No problem" when responding to patients who said, "Thanks so much." She then informally asked patients while waiting for the elevator what impression this made upon them as a fond farewell. On average they gave it a two or three out of five.

Armed with this information, the practice manager conducted a meeting with her team members and informed them of the impact and challenged them to raise the bar. They came up with three phrases they were going to try: *You're welcome*, *It's my pleasure* or *It's my honor*. They outlawed the phrase *No problem* going forward. Patient satisfaction scores immediately showed a positive impact from these changes.

64

Try "Yes, and..."

Disney sometimes hires outside consulting and training companies to help them improve their culture and service. One of those companies we hired when I was a Disney cast member was an improvisational group that had a unique way of communicating business concepts and building and solidifying a team.

I often find many of the best business ideas are the simplest. One of the simplest concepts the improv group taught us was the concept of saying, "Yes, and..." to any idea that was thrown out in a meeting that builds the story instead of shutting it down. It's a classic exercise in the world of improvisational acting whereby actors and comedians can best support one another when building a story in a short scene or skit, not by trouncing on ideas, but rather saying the words, "Yes, and...", and then adding their own ideas. This is a great way to encourage team members to share their ideas freely in a non-threatening environment. It eliminates ridicule and apprehension and helps create a safe space where everyone can contribute, regardless of role or title.

The words "no" and "but..." are conversation and idea killers. If possible, try to avoid using them when someone shares an idea or opinion. And refrain from saying, "Yeah, but!"

As a matter of fact, the word NO by itself is on our list of verbal graffiti, among others including "It's not my job" and "I don't know." (As a reminder, graffiti is the term we use to refer to anything that distracts or detracts from the ideal patient experience.)

Challenge yourself and your team to come up with better ways to respond to common questions and requests. Practice the "Yes, and…" technique to keep the ideas flowing!

Two organizations who really led the way in creating a culture of YES are Ochsner Health System and Dignity Health Medical Foundation. They incorporated YES into their organizational True North statements:

> Ochsner Health System: We create healthcare with peace of mind for our patients, their family members, and each other by Living a Culture of Yes.

> Dignity Health Medical Foundation: We unite healing and humankindness to create peace of mind for every person, every time, through a culture of yes.

> *It does not mean saying yes to everything, but it does challenge everyone to avoid saying the word "NO."*

Human Kindness at Work

"The ultimate outcome of every patient experience is love; whether the patient gets better or not."

- Jake Poore

65

Love is the Best Medicine

Disney's business value proposition is getting their cast members to turn everyday transactions into relationships, the byproduct of which is creating happiness for people of all ages, everywhere. Happiness translates very tangibly into loyalty factors and ultimately, revenue and stock dividends.

Disney successfully combines technical expertise (the product) and service expertise (delivered by an engaged workforce) to create happiness. At Disney:

I started this company, Integrated Loyalty Systems, in 2002, with the sole aim of helping hospitals and health care facilities adapt these same Disney ideals, tenets, and blueprints to healthcare. That's why our tagline and mission is **elevating the human side of healthcare.**

Doctors, medical technologists, and other care professionals have the awe-inspiring ability and responsibility to transform lives through their clinical excellence and expertise. But this is just one side of the important healing equation. The other side is service excellence: the human side. Some call it human kindness. When clinical excellence and service excellence are united to create exceptional patient experiences, that is when true healing takes place. In health care:

Loyalty comes from meeting expectations on the product/clinical side and exceeding expectations on the service side.

Remember, the ultimate outcome of every patient experience is love, whether the patient gets better or not.

66

Build Trust by Connecting with Your Belly Button

It's been said you never get a second chance to make the right first impression. Making eye contact and smiling goes a long way, but for busy people in a high anxiety field like healthcare, the next level in forming relationships is to connect with people umbilically, or lining up your belly button to theirs.

I learned a lot about body language at Disney University and on-the-job training, but I specifically learned this tip from Janine Driver in her book on body language, *You Say More Than You Think*.

This is one of my favorite tips because it's so easy to do, and it can make an immediate positive impact. When speaking with another person, adjust your body frame so your belly button is facing theirs. Lining up your belly button in this manner helps to ensure you're facing them directly, giving them your full attention and respect. Not only does it work, but I get a kick out of thinking about belly buttons!

I see many exam rooms in healthcare where the physician is set up for failure. Often the patient is sitting on an exam table in one corner of the room, and the computer desk is mounted to the wall on the opposite side of the room. The doctor has to turn their back to the patient while asking questions and typing answers into the computer. The unintended consequence is that patient feels like the doctor does not care about them.

Lining up your belly button is also a great altitude indicator. If they're sitting then you sit; if they stand then you stand. As previously discussed, a patient might feel like you're *talking down to them* or *looking down your nose* at them if you approach them from an elevated altitude.

67

Create Special Places for Quiet Moments

Walt Disney World is famous for creating happiness for people of all ages, everywhere. This includes infants and new mothers. Disney has Baby Care Stations in each of its theme parks and a special place just for moms and babies, including rocking chairs, changing tables, and all the accoutrements for nursing, feeding, and changing a baby. Moms tell us it's incredibly appreciated and a great place for a little respite.

Consider offering a private space for your visitors or employees who are nursing mothers. Soft lighting, warm colors, and comfortable chairs all help create an atmosphere of comfort.

It's said that more prayers are uttered in hospitals and airport terminals than in churches. Creating a non-clinical space away from patient activity can offer peace, comfort, and quiet for patients, visitors, families, doctors, nurses, and anyone who needs a quiet moment to get through a trying time.

Many hospitals have chapels or meditation gardens. Some have a rock garden or a walking labyrinth in an outdoor space. If you're not sure what would work at your facility, ask your patients and your employees.

68

Employ Empathy in the Bill Payment Process

In the early 80s, Disney used to have Ticket Sellers and Ticket Takers at what was then Epcot Center. When automated ticket taking machines came along, the human touch stayed. Ticket Takers became Park Greeters and Ticket Sellers morphed into Vacation Planners. Paying for admission is a necessary part of theme park business, but at Walt Disney World, kindness is part of the transaction.

Similarly, in healthcare we have Patient Financial Services. Compassion and empathy should be an integral part of paying for health care. Here's a story we experienced first hand:

We took our 10-year old daughter downtown to the big children's hospital when she became critically ill. We were in an emergency room waiting to be moved to the ICU when a billing representative approached us to fill out the required insurance, payment and authorization forms. Instead of rushing right to the business at hand (paying the bill), this young man took the time to introduce himself and show concern for the well-being of our daughter. He recognized the timing was poor and told us he'd stop back later. He gave words of encouragement. The empathy and kindness he showed to us during a time of incredible stress really made a difference, and we'll always be thankful.

I went with my friend Ken when he was rushed to another ER. One of the first people to see him, before he was stabilized, was someone from patient financial services who came in and asked him how he would like to take care of his $6,000 deductible! He became very angry and his heart rate immediately shot up. He was there for chest pain and hadn't yet been seen by the cardiologist. The timing and manner of this request was poor.

Of course, everyone should pay their fair share, but as you can see from these examples, timing and how billing is handled is very important. At some point, patients and family members will have to speak with an accounting or billing representative to either pay their bill or make payment arrangements. For many families, the billing meeting on top of the hospital visit adds to the stress.

Imagine you only have $500 in your checking account (which is about what many Americans have, on average), you have a credit card with a limit of $3,500, and someone asks you to pay an unexpected $6,000. At least you can save for a couple of years when you go to Disney World, but most people don't typically save for an unexpected trip to the emergency room. It causes high anxiety.

Be sure that your billing and accounting teams understand how to navigate the sometimes difficult conversations that can occur in paying for health care. We can't get rid of bills, but empathy, a kind word, a smile, words of encouragement, proper timing - all of these can lower stress and make family members more receptive to the conversation about payment and medical insurance.

69

Make a Connection

The Walt Disney Company knows that the Disney difference is not in the rides, but in their cast members' ability to interact with guests. To encourage this interactivity, Disney introduced pin trading in the early part of the 1990s. Disney cast members wear a lanyard full of tradable pins and encourage guests to buy their own lanyard and start collecting and swapping pins with cast members.

A version of this in healthcare today comes from Catholic hospitals where nurses wear angel pins on their collars with the intent to give it to one of their patients who needs it the most that day.

It only takes a second to make a connection with another human being. At Disney, we were taught to first make the human connection of eye contact and a smile with everybody we meet. Secondly, we were taught to look for visual clues to help us connect with the person we are serving - perhaps a favorite sports team logo on a shirt or reading the back of the Mickey Mouse ears to learn the child's name (or someone who is a child at heart).

Making a connection is an important part of elevating the human side of healthcare. It creates a bond between caregiver and patient that can lead to greater trust and a greater likelihood that the patient will be more engaged in their own care. Patients who feel like they are partners and feel like they are being cared for are more likely to come back when they need medical care.

This concept is also important for engaging employees, not just patients. Here are two simple ways you can start an immediate connection with patients and employees:

> The **About Me Poster** is a way to connect with patients. Patients or their loved ones can fill these out in their hospital room, with spaces for their preferred name, hobbies and interests.

> A **Personal Profile** or "Favorites Questionaire" is a way to connect with a new employee. It is a questionnaire to discover their likes, dislikes, and overall personal preferences.

As mentioned in an earlier lesson, asking open-ended questions also helps to make connections: "What do you like to do when you're not in the hospital?" Or "What do you like to do when you're not at work?"

It's important that employees and patients feel a sense of worth by being treated as individuals.

Healthcare team members can practice teamwork to help each other create connections. You can leave a little note on the chart about something the patient is interested in or something that recently happened in their family such as a wedding, new baby, or a graduation. When the next person who sees the file brings it up, the patient will think it's magic!

70

Seek the Question Behind the Question

In every business, customers often ask what some might consider silly or seemingly irrelevant questions, like, "Excuse me, do you work here?" The question isn't really whether or not you work here. The question the customer is really asking is, "Can you help me?" A great exercise for every organization is to seek the question behind the question.

There are four levels of answering customer questions:

1. Answering the question in a condescending manner, or laughing at the question. (BAD)

2. Answering the question with minimal additional information. (GOOD)

3. Answering the question in a way that exceeds expectations. (BETTER)

4. Answering the question in a way that delights them and makes it into an experience. (BEST)

Let's apply this using a couple of examples.

One of the most commonly asked questions at Walt Disney World's Magic Kingdom is *"What time is the 3 o'clock parade?"* It might seem like a ridiculous question, but consider what the guest is **really** asking. Disney cast members are trained to answer the question behind the question and then provide additional information.

The guest really wants to know what time the 3 o'clock parade will come by HERE - the spot where they're standing right at that moment. If they're on Main Street now and the parade begins in Frontierland, it won't pass in front of them for about 20 minutes. Armed with this information, the cast member can now answer the question in one of four ways (note the different levels of service with each response):

1. Duh, Mister! It starts at 3 o'clock! (BAD)

2. Well sir, the parade starts at 3 o'clock, but it won't actually arrive here on Main Street until about 3:20 PM. (GOOD)

3. It starts at 3 o'clock, but it won't actually arrive here on Main Street until about 3:20 PM. You may wish to save your spot an hour early since the park is crowded today. (BETTER)

4. It starts at 3 o'clock, but it won't be here until about 3:20 PM. You'll want to save a spot early and if you stand right over there, you will get great pictures of the parade with Cinderella's castle in the background of every shot! And here's a sticker for your child. Have her wear it so the princesses will invite her to dance with them in the parade. (BEST)

That main street balloon seller just elevated the human side of Disney. He knows the difference between his tasks (selling balloons) and his role in the show (We create happiness...). How much did answer #4 cost? How much time did it take? And what impact did it make on that family? Don't stop there! What impact did it make on a cast member who delivered that magic? That one interaction just might have turned a "summer job" into a lifelong Disney career.

Anyone can work in a theme park or a resort hotel, but how many can "create happiness for people of all ages, everywhere?" Magic does not have to cost a lot of time and money, but it does take thought and a concerted effort to earn world-class status.

Consider a mother just spent the night in an emergency exam room with her daughter, who is now stable and resting. The mom is tired and hungry and doesn't want to leave her sleeping daughter's bedside. The nurse tells the mom that the doctor will be stopping by "soon." Still, the mother asks, "What time will the doctor be coming?" The question behind the question if you probed further is *I'm starving, and I want to know if I have time to grab a quick bite to eat so I don't miss the doctor...do I have time? Is there a place nearby to get a cup of coffee and a muffin?*

People don't always say exactly what they mean, but if you apply the technique of looking for the question behind the question, you can raise the patient experience to the next level.

71

Keep the Family Together

A story is often told that Walt Disney would take his two daughters to Griffith Park in California, and then sit on a bench and watch them ride the merry-go-round. In 1998, Sharon Disney Miller spoke of her father to the *San Francisco Chronicle*, and said, "As he stood there, he kept thinking there should be more for parents and children to do <u>together</u>, and the idea for Disneyland was born."

Walt Disney wanted to help families capture the joy and happiness of spending time together. "Together" begins with family-friendly attractions at Disney parks and extends to cast members who recognize the importance of helping families capture the magic.

Once when I was in the Magic Kingdom near Cinderella Castle, I noticed a father attempting to take a picture of his wife and three children in front of the castle. At the same time, I saw a facility services cast member in dark green coveralls walk up to the father and offer to take a photo of the entire family. And the father gratefully accepted!

The truth is - Disney cast members, whoever they are, wherever they work, are trained to stop what they're doing and offer to take the picture so everyone can be in the shot. Keeping the family together is now part of the Disney organization DNA.

Whether you're an individual, a straight or gay couple, or a family of seven from India, the Disney mission is to serve you and keep the family together.

At the Tower of Terror (one of the thrill rides at Disney's Hollywood Studios theme park), when a family shows up and one member of the family isn't quite tall enough to ride, a cast member gives that person a bellman hat and invites them to come "work" so the other family members can enjoy the ride. If there's a baby in the group, there's a nice lounge where one parent can wait with the baby while the other parent rides the ride. Then, they can switch, without having to wait in line again. This way, both parents can enjoy the ride! This "Baby Swap" is available at many of Disney's thrill rides.

Hospitals and healthcare environments also have opportunities to create meaningful connections and should keep the family together as well.

• Consider the new father who wants to stay in the same room as the mother and newborn. Is there a recliner, loveseat, or couch in the patient room that can convert to a sleeping area for the dad? Will it fit an adult? Or is it meant just for sitting? What can be done to accommodate the dad and keep the family together?

• Think of the mom who spent all night at her child's bedside – she may appreciate a warm blanket or pillow, or a cup of coffee in the morning.

• What about the grandfather who wants to cheer up his ailing wife – he may appreciate a clear shelf where he can display pictures of their grandkids and their beloved dog.

• Think about a father who hadn't eaten for over 24 hours because he didn't want to leave his wife's bedside. His nurse went down to the cafeteria during her break and brought the father back a sandwich.

- Or, think of the child whose parent is sick. Often, children are not allowed to visit due to age restrictions or the nature of an illness. Is there a family friendly area where the child could visit with the parent without disturbing other patients?

By putting yourself into a wide variety of patient and family scenarios, you can start to anticipate the needs of all your visitors.

Keeping the family together is important. The patient is always our purpose, but they aren't our only customer. How can you create special moments for patients, family members, or colleagues? How can you keep them all in the picture, so to speak, to create a better patient experience?

72

Practice Active Listening

Active listening is a key component in providing exceptional customer service and is the ultimate sign of respect. Through active listening, you're telling the other person: I hear you. I value you. I seek to understand you.

Active listening is something the Disney characters are trained to do when they interact with children. Princesses and others that can talk can use cues like smiling, eye contact, a head nod, etc. to show active listening. But for the costumed characters that don't speak, such as Pluto, Mickey or Winnie the Pooh, they're trained to bend a knee and get down to the level of the child, give a gentle hug, or give a high five. These subtle, nonverbal cues let kids know their favorite character is fully in the moment with them.

Author Stephen Covey said in his book, *The 7 Habits of Highly Effective People*, "Most people do not listen with the intent to understand; they listen with the intent to reply." Wise words. When someone else is talking, many of us are thinking about what we're going to say instead of using the time to actually gain understanding.

In the 19th century, the great physician William Osler told his students "Listen to the patient, he is telling you the diagnosis." His words are still true today.

Active listening in healthcare is both verbal and nonverbal. Nonverbal listening includes eye-contact, appropriate body language, and using facial expressions that are appropriate to the situation. The verbal part of active listening involves paraphrasing what the patient says, and asking for clarification when necessary. By paraphrasing, the healthcare team member verifies that he or she understands what the patient is saying. By asking for clarification, the healthcare team member can fill in any information gaps and ensure they understand what the patient actually intended to communicate.

73

Hold a Hand

When a child with a serious illness or terminal medical condition visits a Disney theme park, they often have private meetings with the Disney characters. The characters in head-to-toe costumes don't speak to guests, but they do communicate by bending down to the child's level, offering a warm hug, and holding a hand. For a family living with a devastating diagnosis, this small act of kindness means the world.

The simple act of holding another person's hand provides a tremendous opportunity to make a connection. It can be transformational. Without saying a word, you have the power to reassure patients, especially those facing an uncertain or devastating diagnosis. Often, something as simple as holding a patient's hand, taking their hand in yours, or putting a hand on their shoulder can provide tremendous comfort. It shows compassion and empathy and can help build trust between caregivers and patients.

Positive touch is powerful when used wisely. There will be times when you know that holding a patient's hand is a welcome gesture. There are other times where you will want to ask first, or refrain from touching the patient at all.

One physician we worked with found that holding a patient's hand while delivering bad news made a huge impact in patient understanding. He admits that he thought it was hokey at first, but the patients really seemed to like it. So he kept doing it. When he also sat with his patients, made eye contact and focused on listening to his patients, he moved to number one in his medical practice group for patient satisfaction!

Everything Speaks
(Physical Environment)

"Remember, in the eyes, ears, and nose of the patient, everything speaks because everything matters."

- Jake Poore

74

Celebrate Your Legends and Leave a Legacy

Disney connects cast members to one another in a service theme that starts with a collective "WE", by reminding them of the legendary leaders that helped shape the most magical company on earth. If you walk down Main Street U.S.A. at the Magic Kingdom, you can look up on the second floor storefront windows and see the names of the fictitious business owners who are actually Disney legends: such as Roy O. Disney (Walt's brother); Dick Nunis (former chairman of Walt Disney Attractions); Harriet Burns (Disney's first female Imagineer); Marc Davis (one of Walt's original nine animators) and more.

New Disney cast members learn about these people who came before them and about the role each of them played to help shape the Disney history and culture. It's a subtle, yet powerful way to connect current and future employees to the rich legacy of the Disney organization.

In every speech, keynote, or workshop my team and I deliver, we always talk about the importance of leaving a legacy and nurturing a culture of WE. A culture where everyone has each other's back. A culture where everyone knows where the organizational compass is pointing, and everyone is aligned toward the same goal with the same end in mind.

Many years ago, I met with the CEO of Florida Hospital Altamonte here in Central Florida. He told me that after their New Employee Orientation, trainers would bring new employees to meet him. He took that opportunity to tell them that the mission of Florida Hospital Altamonte was to 'extend the healing ministry of Jesus Christ.' And then he challenged each new employee by saying, "If you agree with that mission, will you sign my wall?"

That became a very powerful moment for these new employees! From that moment on, every employee – regardless of personal religious beliefs – was committed to fulfilling the mission of that hospital in service to their patients and their community.

There are other things we can do, too. Consider your exam rooms, meeting rooms, or general gathering areas. Why not take the opportunity to honor your legendary leaders in the same way Disney does and name your rooms after them? If the Sisters of Mercy helped found your hospital, could you name a room or an area after them? Be sure to include a photo, plaque or something in the room that explains to employees and visitors exactly how the room got its name.

These little things serve as connectors. They help patients and visitors understand a bit more about your mission and what you value, and they create a bond with employees that can foster pride, meaning, and a connection to a greater WE. Celebrate your legends and encourage new employees to build and leave their own legacy.

75

Make a Good First Impression

What is a guest's first impression of Walt Disney World before meeting their first Disney cast member? As soon as they drive onto Disney property, they know immediately they are at Disney: the landscaping changes, the signage changes, and it's immaculately clean. They KNOW they're at Disney.

Eight out of 10 people told us for two decades that their first impression of Disney - before they met anybody, bought any food, experienced any attraction - was how clean it was. The Disney environment makes a great first impression.

The first human contact at most Disney theme parks is the parking booth attendant, with a costume (uniform), a name tag over their heart, and a bright Disney smile. Then, there are the parking lot attendants, the parking tram attendants, ticket sellers, security officers, etc. Everyone has a role in adding to that positive first impression.

In healthcare, it's important to remember that first impressions often happen before patients even meet with their provider in the exam or hospital room.

From the first time patients or visitors click on your website, call your office, park in your parking lot, or walk through your door, the patient experience is affected. Every touch point on the patient's journey matters. Everything in your organization "speaks" — from the dead plants in the waiting room, to the employees smoking near the entrance, to a messy desk with confidential files strewn all over it. It's critical to explore things from the patient's viewpoint. What do they see, hear, smell and touch? Consider how all of these things affect the patient experience.

A clean, friendly reception desk with attentive employees makes a good first impression. A welcome mat is an easy first impression. One dermatologist we met decorated his exam room with photos of animals he'd taken during a trip to Africa with his daughter; it was a great first impression, a conversation starter and a way to humanize the exam room.

By mapping out the patient experience, one touch point at a time, and identifying areas for improvement, you'll be able to create great first impressions, always.

76

Become Picture Perfect

As we continue on the journey of creating a culture of always, we must strive to make the invisible, visible and the implicit, explicit. A great way to do that is to create a picture-perfect photo album of your work area or department. When we begin to look through the lens of the patients' eyes, imagine if the lens were attached to a camera?

If you visit any popular restaurant chain like Olive Garden, The Cheesecake Factory, or Chili's and ask them for their training book, they'll show you a book full of pictures of how each dish should be cooked, plated, and served for every customer, every time. Disney uses this same methodology to create consistency in their delivery processes. I believe healthcare delivery systems need to adopt this process as well.

At Disney hotels around the world, as all guests are fast asleep in their hotel rooms at night, a crew of housekeeping team members is transforming each lobby by vacuuming, wiping, cleaning, and rearranging the furniture from floor to ceiling. How do they reset each back to being picture-perfect? How do supervisors know that the room is picture-perfect? How do the environmental services team members know what chemicals should be used for every piece of furniture, picture frame, countertop, and floor? They rely on their picture-perfect photo album.

So, as a new employee of Environmental Services, when you arrive at midnight to clean the lobby of your hospital and the waiting areas on three separate floors, how do you know how the chairs should be arranged? What chemicals should you use? What signs should or should not be up? And what brochures should or should not be there? What should or should not be on the front desk at check-in at 8:00 AM? Perhaps you need a picture-perfect photo album.

Many organizations use a similar process for communicating standards of dress, often in the form of side-by-side photos in a picture-perfect album showing what is acceptable and what is not. Remember that everything speaks - and the appearance of employees is part of the story.

77

Disney Streetmosphere Meets Atmo Amy

Disney is famous for a lot of things, but one of the things that many visiting guests may take for granted are what Disney calls "Streetmosphere" characters. These are professional theme park performers that enhance the atmosphere of the street, or "Streetmosphere." These performers are excellent with scripted, highly interactive skits and improvisation. Streetmosphere characters may be dressed as police officers, taxi cab drivers, janitors, magicians, or other entertainers that all seek to create a positive atmosphere that enhances that specific scene, street or land at various locations throughout Walt Disney World Resort.

You may find a comedy troupe in front of the United Kingdom or Italy pavilion at Epcot; a magician or 1930s Hollywood film crew working the streets of Hollywood Boulevard at Disney's Hollywood Studios; or the Mayor on Main Street U.S.A. in the Magic Kingdom. Their trade is the art of creating positive distractions and memorable interactions. As corny as many of them can be, you can't help but to smile. And isn't that the point at the *happiest place on earth*?

We took this concept of Disney Streetmosphere characters and adapted it to the hospital Emergency Department setting. We recognized that **while the primary role for doctors and nurses was to take care of the patient, who was taking care of everyone else that came with the**

patient? And who was keeping the patient in the loop on delays?

The goal was to try to relieve some of the high-anxiety and lack of information that is pervasive in emergency medicine, or maybe even put a smile on someone's face. We worked with Renee Rountree, Chief Experience Officer at Riverside Health System in Newport News, Virginia. Renee immediately grasped the concept and found one of the nicest hospital volunteers with the biggest smile to help test our hypothesis. She found Amy, a young, very friendly mother of four, and asked her to help with this new project.

As a volunteer and avid Disney visitor herself, Amy understood Disney's proactively friendly approach and did a great job taking care of the patients and their family members throughout the hospital. In the emergency department, Amy would visit patients in their exam rooms and offer to make them as comfortable as possible, offering many of the non-clinical creature comforts that most of us desire: an extra blanket or pillow, a magazine or help making a phone call or assistance adjusting the television.

Of course, she could not offer patients any food or drink until the doctor completed an exam, but she could offer a cup of hot coffee or bottled water to folks who were there with patients. She would even help distract patients' children by coloring with them in the waiting area.

Amy was immediately appreciated by patients and staff. Amy also became an informal expediter - asked to help check on the care status if the wait was getting too long. She was so successful improving the care atmosphere, she was nicknamed "Atmo Amy" (creating the right atmosphere for healing and working), and Ms. Rountree got justification to hire two full-time employees to replace Amy's temporary, volunteer position.

The goal was to decrease anxiety and complaints, and increase warmth and patient satisfaction. Results showed that each day Amy volunteered, complaints went down and satisfaction went up. Not just patient satisfaction, but employee satisfaction as well! By implementing this full time position, Riverside Health discovered that **"although the patient may be our purpose...they're not our only customer."** It also revealed that if you take care of the family caregiver, they will also help take care of the patient experience (and many times they are the ones filling out the patient satisfaction survey). Although Amy no longer works there, the warm and helpful atmosphere she created carries on.

So what price would you place on a simple kind word given to your mother when she is laying there, all alone in the Emergency Room? What about a prayer, a warm hug, someone calling you and giving you updates until you can get there? Exactly. Even though it should be everyone's job to comfort and keep the patient and family informed, isn't nice to know that when things get busy, there is someone whose sole responsibility to get that done? And we're always busy...everyday! So, go find yourself an Atmo Amy or Atmo Andy today! Someone whose entire role is the art of creating positive distractions and a caring atmosphere.

78

Expand the Procedure to Include the Entire Experience

Every cast member has a role in the show at Disney, and the show is to create happiness – not just to provide a bunch of *attractions*. If you ask the average family who has never been to a Disney theme park why they're going, most people will say they're going to ride the rides. After their Disney vacation, if you ask that same family what will make them come back, they'll tell you all about the little details of their entire Disney experience.

Disney has learned a lesson that many of their competitors have not, and that is the need to expand the ride to include the entire experience. Every step on the Disney vacation journey is an opportunity to make or break the family's decision on whether they intend to return.

Disney is not just a master of the show. They are masters of the **entire experience,** which includes the show.

In healthcare, we can't just be masters of our individual show, such as surgery, physical therapy, or hospice. We also have to be masters of the entire patient experience. The real wow factor at Disney does not come from one magical interaction, it comes from the sum of all interactions.

Most healthcare providers do an excellent job of providing quality clinical care. Now is the time to provide the same standard of quality to the entire patient experience: from your website, to your campus signage, to parking, to admissions, to all the interactions with healthcare providers, and on through to discharge.

Every step of the patient journey adds to the patient's perception of the facility, services, and of the quality of care. Those perceptions influence how patients talk about the experience when they are back out in the community - and if they would choose your facility and services in the future.

The "patient experience" describes how patients evaluate their encounters with the healthcare system, generally framed by their expectations of how they want to be treated and how they are treated at other organizations where they pay money (hotels, department stores, restaurants). A patient's experience is affected by four influences - people, processes, product and physical environment.

The Patient Experience

The "patient experience" is how patients evaluate their encounters, framed by their expectations of how they <u>want</u> to be treated and how they are treated at other organizations, and affected by both the clinical and human interactions with your people, processes, product and physical environment.

79

Use the Art of
Positive Distraction

Disney is famous for their Hidden Mickeys. Have you ever spotted one? Hidden Mickeys are hidden images of a Mickey Mouse silhouette that have been incorporated into the design of murals, planters, pictures, and in the pre-show queues so families can compete with one another in a "Where's Waldo" type of game. It's fun for families, and it's a great way to pass the time in lines that are often quite long.

When you check in at the front desk of Disney's Wilderness Lodge Resort, adults rest their elbows on the marble top front desk. However, children who are 48" or smaller can discover hidden forest animals carved in brass underneath the counter.

At all of the Disney resort hotels, there are small, semi-private areas set up just off to the side of the front desk dedicated exclusively to children. The furniture is small and kid-sized and the TV is playing a classic Disney cartoon movie. It's an inviting space where kids are occupied (within Mom and Dad's eyesight) while their parents check in.

So what does all of this have to do with healthcare? Healthcare could learn a lot from Disney's art of positive distraction. Sometimes you see a "Where's Waldo" poster in the waiting area, but for the most part, healthcare does a poor job positively distracting people from the wait time experience.

The ambulances at Florida Hospital for Children feature DVD players that can play music or videos while children are transported to and from the hospital. At Nemours Children's Hospital in Orlando, Florida, all of the hospital room walls are painted white for a reason. If the patients want to change the color of their room, they can - they just choose a color and a filter on the light changes the color of the room to easily accommodate the wishes of young patients.

Most pediatricians' offices have a play area for children. But what about in primary care or hospital settings? Children often accompany adults to appointments or for visits. You don't need a bunch of toys or a huge area dedicated to kids; you just something to make them feel welcome while distracting them from the wait time. It can be as simple as a small table with some crayons and pages to color, or maybe some blocks or hand puppets.

The University of Pittsburgh Medical Center Children's Hospital positively distracts patients by turning the MRI machine into a jungle story. Children are not only positively distracted by the decorations and decor, they are told they are on a secret mission through the jungle on a canoe, and they must remain perfectly still. Patient satisfaction scores went up 90%.[3]

Any positive distraction that temporarily occupies a child's attention or eases their fear can also reduce angst for their parents. In addition to meeting the child's needs, you'll be surprised to learn that adults will also appreciate this thoughtful gesture.

80

Let Form Follow Function

Building on the concept of the art of positive distraction, you may have heard of the architectural philosophy 'form follows function.' The form is the art, aesthetics, or décor, and the function is how it's used. A classic example is a clock on the wall. The form is the decoration/design of the clock and the function is that it tells the time.

Why are there so few clocks at Disney? The function that Disney is trying to create is an illusion of time. They want to transport you in their time machine to a fantasy world or to a galactic planet. The only time they typically use clocks is when the form follows the function. Main Street U.S.A. has a clock on the city hall. The German pavilion at Epcot has a cuckoo clock where a boy in lederhosen comes out and rings the bell every hour. In many cases, the absence of clocks also creates a function. The function is an illusion of time.

When I visit pediatric exam rooms, I often find that every exam room has a school-like clock hanging over each patient bed. I asked the leader, "Why would you hang a clock over the patient's bed?" She replied, "That's so our staff can write down the time when they administer medicines and do different procedures" (staff-driven).

While that may be very helpful for their internal processes, you need to consider who typically accompanies each child. The parents, right? So what are the parents going to do for three straight hours while they're waiting with their child? They'll not only watch the second hand, but they'll hear it tic-tic-tic. This is the 21st century where everybody has a smart phone or some device that can tell them the time. Let's figure out a way to be more patient-driven. Perhaps one way might be to replace the school-type clocks with a digital clock.

Recently, I was at a brand new pediatric emergency room where they ironically used Mickey, Minnie, Daisy, and Donald decals to decorate the exam room. "The form is Mickey and Minnie entertainment, but what is the function?" I asked. The Director of the Emergency Room replied, "It's just to make kids smile."

I had an idea to raise the function to a higher level than just to make kids smile. So to test it, we brought a child into the room and had him lay down on the exam table. We put one of the Mickey decals on the ceiling so he had something to look at. Then, when we wanted to look in his right ear we put a Minnie decal on the wall for him to look at – right in the exact spot where we wanted him to turn his head. We put a Daisy decal where we wanted him to look when we checked his left ear. Finally, we put a Donald Duck decal on the wall where we wanted him to look as we checked his eyes. And everyone loved it! It was a win-win for the staff, patient and parents.

81

Use Theming to Tell a Story

Very few hospitals have floors or departments that are themed and that tell a story. To play on our last lesson, they're good on function, but not so much on form.

Disney's Magic Kingdom park is laid out in different lands themed to a specific time in history or imaginary place: Adventureland, Fantasyland, Tomorrowland, Liberty Square, and more. Each land has its own theme and everything fits the theme, including the trash cans, architecture, music, landscaping, benches, and costumes. Anything that doesn't fit the theme is what Disney calls a "visual intrusion." At my company, Integrated Loyalty Systems, we call it "visual graffiti."

If you go to Frontierland at the Magic Kingdom, you'll see that the color of the pavement looks like a muddy cowboy town, and there are wood planks on the sidewalks. The music changes between lands, and sometimes, the smells do too (you're sure to smell popcorn as you pass the movie marquees at the park entrance).

Disney characters always have meet and greets in their specific lands, which is why you would never see Cinderella in Tomorrowland. She's always in Fantasyland, near her castle.

Most healthcare providers have things for children...stars, space rockets, teddy bears - but without a theme. Even the stickers given away to kids are not a part of the theme; they're just whatever was ordered. Dora stickers are given away in a rocket room. Nothing fits. It doesn't tell a story. In the children's hospital I recently visited, you could park on the red rocket floor or the pink pony floor, but what did it mean? It should tell a story.

The emergency room at Riverside Health System in Newport News, Virginia, tells a story - but that wasn't always the case. Years ago, when they were redoing their emergency room facilities, the ER director had three goals in mind. He wanted to create an environment that would welcome patients and visitors, serve as a positive distraction for patients dealing with pain and anxiety, and celebrate and honor their community.

He began by searching for a way to add a few human elements to their exam rooms, which were all named after the architectural quadrants from the blueprints: 1-3-41, 1-3-42, etc. From a facilities standpoint, this labeling was logical and indicated what floor and quadrant each room was on. But to patients and care team members, the naming system didn't make any sense at all. It was impersonal and, quite often, confusing.

One of the things the Riverside community is known for is their beautiful waterways. The director saw this as a great opportunity to elevate the community and raise employee pride. As it turns out, there was a Riverside physician who just happened to be an avid photographer. The director asked him to take professional-looking black and white photographs around the area, which were then used to theme each room to local waterways: Chesapeake Bay, Riverside, the Atlantic Ocean, etc.

Not only did this physician take pictures for the Emergency Room, but he signed every picture as well. Now the rooms are named and themed with local waterways, and patients can enjoy the photos that are signed by the doctor hanging on the wall while they're waiting.

Even if your budget doesn't allow for theming to the extent that Disney does it, there are still some things that can be done. What color are the walls in your hospital or facility? Are they bland and white? That can make it feel too sterile and not very welcoming. Color their world! Choose colors, images, photos, or pictures for the walls in colors that evoke the feeling you're looking for and that create a healing ambience.

In a rehabilitation hospital, perhaps you'd like bright colors to get them out of bed. In a long-term care facility, you may opt for more cheerful colors. Did you know that in the world of color, yellows and greens can evoke feelings of love, trust, acceptance, joy, and optimism? In a behavioral health or drug rehabilitation unit, you want colors that have a calming effect. Choose colors that can put people at ease.

82

Do you Need a Mascot?

The Walt Disney Company is very protective of their character images, and for good reason. Registered and trademarked characters represent the Disney brand, and value of the brand is an important asset to the company. Consider the power and appeal of Mickey Mouse, the most recognized cartoon character in the world. When you see Mickey Mouse, you are reminded of "the happiest place on Earth!" Mickey is the Disney company mascot, and as such, is integral to the Disney brand.

Hospitals and healthcare providers also have a brand. Your brand is how you are perceived, or want to be perceived, by the community you serve. Symbols or logos help illustrate the brand. Another effective way to market your brand is with a mascot.

Mascots aren't just for sports teams anymore! They can offer similar benefits for hospitals and their employees. Mascots are fun! They can be your team's cheerleaders, encouraging your employees to let their hair down and celebrate the good things you're doing.

A hospital mascot can be a spokesperson or representative of your organization. Usually a mascot is an excellent way to get attention and promote the values of your organization. Done well, your mascot can market your hospital and share your message in a format that is effective and memorable, and the element of whimsy from your mascot can create balance in the life-or-death world of health care.

Mascots are especially effective when caring for your pediatric patients. Fear is a normal reaction by most children when they are hospitalized, and often a friendly, costumed character can lighten the mood and create a cheerful approach to patient care.

One of our clients, Medstar National Rehabilitation Hospital, has an effective mascot named Vic. Vic (short for victory) serves as a reminder of the many small victories achieved in rehabilitation medicine. Vic is just as important to Medstar employees as he is to the patients, and serves as a proud reminder to the healthcare team of their commitment to excellent customer service and the highest quality patient care.

83

Enhance an Experience with Music

Think about your favorite movie. The use of music in that movie has the power to create and accentuate the right mood throughout the movie. Walt Disney understood this in movie making, and he applied it when he launched his first theme park in 1955. He could build the most wonderful place in the world, AND he could use music to enhance it.

When you walk down Main Street U.S.A. at the Magic Kingdom, the music is from turn-of-the-century America. It's upbeat, fun, and matches what you want to do, which is to keep moving and start your adventure. When you walk into Future World at Epcot, you hear symphonic music with a futuristic feel. Walk through France at Epcot and you'll hear romantic music that makes you feel like you just arrived in Paris.

The right music can set the mood and tone in subtle ways. When it's right, you hardly notice it. But when it's wrong, it feels out of place and awkward.

The waiting area of a hospital or care facility is often a dark and lonely place for families of patients. Rather than having nothing playing at all or an episode from Jerry Springer on the television, why not choose something that might be a little more soothing and relaxing? For example, at a large primary care clinic in

California, they've purchased Muzak, and they ask patients when they check in what type of music they'd like to hear.

Research has shown that music plays an important part in healing, which is why organizations like Cleveland Clinic have invested heavily in music therapy.

Celebration Hospital in Florida has an MRI decorated to look like a sand castle as part of a beach theme. Your changing rooms are cabanas, and you'll hear beach music playing softly in the background.

Along with the wall color, the furniture and other details of your waiting area, the music is all part of the overall experience. The right music can create the right ambience for the right healing experience. Think about the different emotions of waiting for a cancer treatment, or in the end-of-life room near the chapel, or waiting for a burger in the cafeteria. There are different emotional hot-spots throughout the hospital, and we could use music to accentuate or calm those emotions. Your choice of music will affect the patient and family member experience.

84

Perpetuate a Culture of Always in the Physical Environment

In Frontierland at the Magic Kingdom, everything looks rustic to evoke a feeling of the Old West. In Fantasyland, everything is colorful and whimsical. Now imagine you're visiting Frontierland and you see a Disney cast member walk by in a futuristic-looking space suit on her way to her shift at Space Mountain. Or, perhaps you're in Fantasyland complete with a soaring castle, flying elephants and whirling teacups...and suddenly you see a cowboy sporting boots, a lasso and a ten-gallon hat on his way to his shift at Big Thunder Mountain Railroad.

None of these scenarios would ever actually happen at a Disney theme park. Why? Because not only would it ruin the magic for park guests, it would also be very confusing. Disney would call this a visual intrusion or "bad show."

In healthcare, the same thing is true when patients see various care team members in different uniforms with no uniformity. This may seem insignificant, but in the eyes of the patient (and their family members), this is huge.

Every day in a hospital, patients interact with ten or more clinical or non-clinical care team members. However, most patients have no idea what each care team member does based upon what they're wearing. In some hospitals, everyone wears blue scrubs (surgeons, nurses, environmental services, etc.) If you ask an average patient, they would say, "It would be nice to know who's who in healthcare based upon what they're wearing." It adds greater peace of mind. We did this in one emergency department, where we had a poster of "Who's Who In The Emergency Room?" above each exam room bed, which identified each role on the care team based on what uniform they were wearing — nurse, respiratory tech, PA, RN, etc. Only nurses wore red. Each role wore a specific color.

One time my wife was in the emergency room in a lot of pain, and she asked me to get the doctor. As I stepped out of the room and looked down the hallway, I saw ten different hospital workers. I had no idea who was a doctor and who was not.

The first person I stopped was a gentleman in a blue scrub top and pants (who looked like a surgeon). I said, "Doctor, could you help me? My wife is in a lot of pain." And he laughed and said, "Dude, I'm just an environmental services worker," and he went on to clean an exam room. These are the unintentional consequences from a culture of ambiguity that impacts the patient experience.

85

Creatively Hide Your "Bad Show"

Many healthcare workers are desensitized from noticing their own dirty laundry. Since I grew up at Disney, I don't have the same set of eyes. Unfortunately, when I walk through the halls of a hospital I often see clutter made up of computers on wheels, patient beds, laundry carts, housekeeping carts, crash carts, and food service tray carts. In waiting areas, I find coffee cups, newspapers and chairs everywhere. Front desks are overloaded with pamphlets, brochures, and computer monitors that block interaction with the person behind the screen. These are all visual intrusions.

Surgery patients have even told us that when they were scheduled for surgery late in the day they saw a hallway lined with previously used surgical tables with dirty laundry piled on top and draped with a clean sheet. To the untrained eye, this looks like a hallway full of dead bodies. Not the kind of thing you want to see just before your operation.

Good Show, Bad Show

This goes back to Disney's concept of onstage and backstage. Did you know that the Magic Kingdom in Walt Disney World is on the second floor? There is an entire floor below hiding all utilities, supplies, and dirty laundry from the public. These are out of guests' view so as not to distract from the enjoyment of the park.

Anything that detracts, defaces, or distracts from the ideal guest experience at Disney is considered "bad show."

At Integrated Loyalty Systems, we refer to anything that detracts, defaces or distracts from the ideal patient and family experience as "physical graffiti." Of course, not every organization can build back hallways and hide everything from the public, but you can look for creative things you can do to disguise your utilities and dirty laundry to preserve the patient experience For instance, decorative fencing hides ugly trash dumpsters. Plants, bushes, or small trees can camouflage utilities and outdoor employee break areas. Elevators can be designated guest-only elevators.

We use the term dirty laundry to address all the things patients should not see. I have seen security officers eating and drinking at their station. No eating, drinking, smoking, or chewing gum should ever be allowed onstage.

Disney hotel housekeepers bag dirty laundry and immediately remove it by putting it into carts. Disney designed its own laundry carts that have accordion-like doors that are opened and closed by the housekeeper as needed.

Why? Because that's onstage. I call most housekeeping carts used in hospitals the "bare minimum carts" because they have brooms and mops and everything sticking out of them. Disney's carts hide everything and are often even motorized so they can carry more.

Look at the hallway walls on some patient floors, and you'll see quality data, safety data, number of patient falls, employee photographs, and other things that many patients and visitors would consider are "employee-first" and not "patient-first." When you go to any typical floor of a hotel, you will not see any of that on the walls.

A great place to start in identifying dirty laundry is to take photographs of your hallways and your walls through the patients' lens and ask if what you see is for the patients' benefit or for the employees' benefit. Then, challenge your team to find solutions to make the physical environment more patient-driven.

86

Don't Pass Trash

Professor Leonard Berry of Texas A&M says, "Patients are experts of what they know and understand, and they'll judge us on what they do not know and understand." Patients are experts of cleanliness. People know when something's clean or dirty. If you take an elderly grandmother to a hospital cafeteria and she has to go through seven dirty spoons before finding a clean one, she's no longer thinking about spoons. She's thinking, "Gosh, I hope they cleaned the surgical instruments before my surgery."

Have you ever seen a Disney cast member walk past a piece of trash on the ground? The answer is probably no. At Disney, picking up trash isn't just the responsibility of the custodial team; it's everyone's job. It demonstrates teamwork and a common purpose. In fact, the culture at Disney is so strong that even when cast members no longer work for Disney, they're still driven to pick up trash!

When we work with clients we conduct a patient experience and employee cultural assessment. Part of that assessment is what we call a Pride Audit. In other words, we measure how proud your employees are to work in your healthcare facility. One aspect of the Pride Audit is whether employees pick up trash in the hallways. The results may surprise you.

We place an unused coffee cup within four feet of a trash can in high traffic hallways and we count how many employees walk over, around, or kick the trash before one employee picks it up.

Unfortunately, it takes an average of 22 employees and quite a bit of time before someone finally picks up the trash. If providing exceptional patient experiences is everyone's responsibility, then shouldn't it be everyone's job to ensure the facility is clean and safe for patients?

Some medical centers have begun adding "clean up centers" where rubber gloves (I call them no excuse gloves) and trash cans are placed in parking lots and near key entrances of the facility. This encourages team members to pick up trash without having to use their bare hands.

87

Pay Attention to the Details

Disney theme parks and resorts are magical, and it takes people to make the magic happen. Paying attention to the smallest of details is one way Disney preserves the magic that guests have come to expect. Each evening after the parks close, a team of cast members repaints, repairs, and fixes all of the things that aren't picture perfect and may be distracting to the guest experience.

My wife used to work on the Disney Show Quality Team at Epcot, where she and others on the team would meet regularly to conduct a walk-through of the park and report anything needing repainting, repairing or updating.

> **When patients see things in your hospital that don't seem quite right, they may lose confidence in you.**

Patients have expectations when they visit your hospital or care facility. When they see things that aren't quite right, they may lose confidence in the care they're about to receive from you and your team.

What can you do? For starters, fix the leaky faucet, or the chipped paint, or the broken door handle, or whatever small problem is detracting from the experience of your patients (and your employees). And if you can't fix it, find someone who can.

I remember seeing dead plants in a patient waiting room. If a patient or their family member sees any dead plants in the waiting room, they begin to wonder - if they can't even take care of the plants here, how are they going to take care of my loved one?

Take the time to notice the details and make sure they are sending the message you want to be sent.

88

Clean Floors = Clean Operating Rooms
(*In the minds of your patients*)

When I was a child, I remember the big deal in our family was "family night out" because it did not happen very often. Dinner in a real restaurant was a big deal for a family of nine, mostly because it was so expensive for a family our size. Since my mother got paid every other Friday, it was on that day that my parents would load all seven of us kids into the car and drive us to a nice restaurant. However, when we got to the restaurant, my mother would typically make us wait in the car while she scoped the place out. I figured she was checking the menu for affordability. Many times she would return to the car smiling, and we all went in and enjoyed a nice meal. Other times she would jump back into the car and drive us to another restaurant.

What exactly was she "scoping out" anyway? Later in life, I asked her. She said she was looking at the restrooms. Why would a mother of seven want to inspect a restaurant's restrooms? Because in her mind, dirty restrooms meant dirty kitchens. And dirty kitchens meant dirty food.

Everything Speaks!

The last thing my mother wanted to see was one or more of her kids get sick after a nice meal. She felt that if the restrooms weren't clean, she couldn't trust them to serve food to her children.

Do you know the second place most patients go to after entering your hospital's main entrance? That's right, the restrooms! Many patients have to travel a distance to get there. If you follow them (and I do), your patients walk up to your main information desk and ask, "Can you tell me where the restrooms are?"

So the question becomes, what is their first impression when entering your restrooms? Do they say, "Eww" or "Ahh, that's nice." We must remember that in the minds of our patients and visitors, dirty restrooms equals dirty operating rooms. And the cleanliness of the restrooms are absolutely within your control. What a simple opportunity to build trust and peace of mind rather than unintentionally erode it.

A final illustration of the power of cleanliness happened while I was working with Ochsner Health System in New Orleans. I was told a story about a couple who were on vacation when Hurricane Katrina hit. The husband, a physician, brought his sick wife to Ochsner's main hospital. As they entered the main entrance, his wife was both nervous and scared, and she held his hand tightly. But as they walked down the main hallway that led to the Emergency Department, she looked around and said, "I'm going to be just fine here. Look at how clean the floors are! Any organization who takes this much pride and care of their floors while in the midst of a hurricane can surely take care of me and the rest of their patients."

89

Give Patients Choices

As we mentioned in our introduction, there are many differences between the hospitality industry and the healthcare industry. One big difference is that most vacations are planned events and most hospital stays are not. Also, the healthcare industry is wrought with constraints on their ability to personalize or customize customer requests or preferences, especially when linked to the patient's ability to pay. Nevertheless, most people want choices or at least the perception of choice. So what can you do to create a sense of control for patients?

From the very first click on the website or telephone call to Disney's central reservation's office (CRO), Disney strives to give you control, helping you personalize your stay to create your dream vacation. They guide you through a myriad of choices: from the type of resort and location, to the hotel room type, size, view, and length of stay - to meal plans, to character greetings, to theme park tickets and special events. The Disney reservation cast members are more like vacation planners than just employees taking hotel reservation requests. One is proactive and mission-driven, and the other is reactive and task driven.

Patients, on the other hand, rarely anticipate a trip to the hospital and rarely have many choices during that stay. We don't allow them to wear their own clothes. Instead, we give them a patient gown to wear. We replace their name with a patient ID number. We put them in a room that's not really their room, it's room number 314…and then we leave the door open!

- What do they eat? *What we give them.*

- When do they eat? *When we feed them.*

- When can they go to the restroom? *When we answer their call bell.*

- When is that? *When we get there.*

So giving patients choices — any choice — is a big deal to them and their family. You see, people don't change when they go to the hospital, they are still the same people used to living a life full of choices and given a sense of control.

Penn Medicine understands this concern. The University of Pennsylvania Health System (Penn Medicine) received a financial endowment for replacing the old framed art in the building and patient rooms with new art. Rather than just discarding the old art, they repurposed it and created an "art cart." An art cart is a cart filled with framed art pushed room-to-room by a volunteer who offers to patients if they would prefer another piece of art on the wall instead of the one they already have. It provides the patient with a variety of choices and a positive, distracting conversation for the day.

As previously mentioned, Nemours Children's Hospital in Orlando encourages children to change the color of the room's lighting by changing the filter on the light. It makes the ceiling and walls look like a different color, and more importantly, gives the child an element of control in a world where they seldom have any.

Presenting patients with small choices can go a long way in empowering them with a sense of control in an environment where they rarely have any...helping to enable healthcare with peace of mind.

You see, people don't change when they go to the hospital, they are still the same people used to living a life full of choices and given a sense of control.

90

Patient Belongings Bags

Imagine your loved one has just passed away at the hospital. You're overwhelmed with grief and sadness and you have a million things running through your mind. Then, a well-meaning hospital employee hands you a clear plastic bag filled with your loved one's personal belongings including jewelry, wallet, clothes, false teeth, and personal hygiene products.

A bit impersonal? Yes. And it could feel like an invasion of privacy if you had to carry out your loved one's personal belongings in a clear plastic bag for the world to see!

I'll never forget when my grandmother passed away in a long-term care facility in upstate New York. When I went there to collect her things, I was greeted with sympathy by an executive of the facility who proceeded to hand me all of my grandmother's personal belongings in a black twisty-tie trash bag. I was horrified! On top of feeling the sadness that she was gone, I felt angry that they thought so little of her that they would put all of her important worldly processions into a trash bag! I said to the executive, "You thought so much of my grandmother you put all her worldly possessions into a trash bag?" Surprised and a bit taken back, they said, "Trash bag? That's not a trash bag. That's our patient belongings bag. We've always done it that way."

I delivered the eulogy at my grandmother's funeral and I told that story. To me, that bag was not a fond farewell to the lady I loved, but a hurtful result of a business not paying attention to the little details.

A few months later, I felt bad for telling that story. My team and I went back to that business and helped them create a fond farewell box, where we placed all of a patient's personal belongings into the box, wrapped it in a hand-made quilt made by the ladies auxiliary, tied it with a yellow ribbon, and added a sympathy card inside the box signed by everyone on the care team. What a difference it makes to show you care at important moments that matter. People tend to remember their first impression and their last impression.

91

Quiet Please!

When patients remark that it is difficult to sleep, a common caregiver response that's been around for decades in healthcare is, "Oh, you don't sleep in the hospital!" Scientists know that sleep is incredibly important to the healing process, and lack of sleep inhibits that process. The body literally heals itself when you sleep, and yet, it's hard to get good sleep in a hospital. Patients are awakened frequently. Often it's necessary - but not always. And it's mainly on the caregiver's schedule, not the patients.

Hotels don't make you sleep with your door open to the hallway. That would be ridiculous! So why do we do it in healthcare almost every day? How likely would you be to return to a hotel that did that? Nighttime is often a good time to take care of things when there aren't too many people around. But you almost never hear overhead paging, vacuuming, or garbage truck sounds while you're sleeping in a hotel or at a Disney resort. Why? Because it's what Disney calls 'bad show.' It would be an audible intrusion to the ideal guest experience.

Disney embraces the standard practice used by every hotel in America of the Do Not Disturb sign. Clearly, the purpose is to allow the guest to choose when they want their room cleaned or not. This allows a late check-in guest to sleep in, undisturbed, compared to a business guest who leaves early in the morning.

Hospital noise can impede the patients' ability to sleep. Listen with a patient's ear. What do you hear at midnight? At 3:00 AM? Is your unit a quiet and restful place where sleep and healing are taking place? Or are equipment alarms ringing, doors banging, loud conversations happening at the nurses station, or shouting down the hall? When team members enter a patient's room at night, do they flip on all the lights or use the minimal amount of light possible while working quietly and safely?

There is a question on the government-mandated HCAHPS patient satisfaction survey that specifically addresses the noise level patients experience: *During this hospital stay, how often was the area around your room quiet at night? Never? Sometimes? Usually? Or, Always?*

There are several free decibel meter apps that you can download to your smart phone. Use it to measure just how loud things can get around your patients' rooms and then take steps to reduce or eliminate any unnecessary noise at nighttime so your patients can get the healing rest they need.

A growing trend in healthcare in America is to take a page from Disney and others' playbook and go back to the good, old-fashioned Do Not Disturb sign. Another hospital allows patients to choose whether they prefer their door to be left open or closed.

Additionally, hospitals that want to create more opportunities for sleep for their patients can provide ear plugs or eye covers, and will offer to dim the lights to help them sleep. One hospital we visited makes a nightly announcement at the start of quiet time. The hallway lights at this hospital are dimmed or off from 9:00 PM until 7:00 AM as a visual reminder to everyone to respect those patients who are trying to rest and heal.

Safety is always the first priority, however, when safety is not an issue, courtesy should be next.

Culture

"The key to making common sense common practice is when the employees and physicians think it's their idea: when you can engage their heart in storytelling and their head in data, then their hands will follow."

- Jake Poore

92

Become Patient Driven

When I first got into healthcare some twenty years ago, I would attend hospital meetings and hear phrases like, "patient centered" or "patient focused." Unclear, I would ask, "what does that mean?" And they would say, "we are putting patients in the center of everything we do."

Confused, I would say, "Really? How do you know that...where are they right now? Where are the patients? Why are they not here in this meeting as we struggle to decide what to do for them next? Shouldn't they help us validate the direction we head to next?" Well intended, they would always talk about them like they were in the room, but they weren't. So how do we become more patient driven, not just patient focused? How do we put the patient in the driver's seat, not just seated at the back of the healthcare bus?

At the Walt Disney World Resort, becoming guest driven was always a major focal point for the organization. Constantly checking in with the guests and staying focused on our service theme was key.

"We create happiness" for guests is more than just an internal slogan or statement of purpose for Disney cast members - it's woven into their organizational DNA and embedded into every action and every decision made throughout the organization. Founder, Walter Elias Disney, always insisted that if everyone focuses their efforts on taking care of the guest and their entire experience, the rest (like finances) should take care of itself. Imagine 74,000 cast members at Walt Disney World putting the guest in the driver's seat of everything they do. Constantly checking in with the guest to make sure you're on the right track of "creating happiness." That is guest driven.

In today's healthcare landscape, however, there seems to be an over-emphasis and focus on patient satisfaction survey scores rather than the patient's actual experience. And that's risky because many organizations focus solely on raising satisfaction scores without building the infrastructure needed to support it or a culture that helps to sustain it. Unless you align all your employees toward a common end-in-mind and change your service culture, your survey results will be month-to-month peaks and valleys. You won't know why you got to the 90th percentile one month and 10th percentile the next. You must become patient-driven, not just patient-centered or patient-focused.

I remember taking a group of business executives on an early-morning tour of one of the Disney parks before it opened for the day. I had just explained that while not every Disney cast member may have memorized the Disney mission, vision or values, every one of them knew that their job was to "create happiness." As we walked down the street, we approached a cast member who was pressure-washing the sidewalk and one of the business executives asked him, "What do you do here?" The cast member's response, "*I make people happy...by keeping this place squeaky clean.*"

Being patient-driven can't just be something you do, it has to be who you are as an organization. Stop any employee in a hospital and ask them what they do, and they will most likely tell you their job title or department (*I'm a nurse, respiratory tech, EVS, radiologist, etc.*), but what you really want is for them to respond with your organization's uniting purpose (*I'm part of a team extending Christ's Ministry*).

One way to engage patients is to ask them what they like or dislike about their current experience. What's working and what isn't working. And what could be improved. Patient focus groups or patient and family advisory councils are great ways to create a safe environment where an organization's leaders can move through every touchpoint on the patient experience journey and ask them what's working, what's not working, and what they think would make it better.

This is what is meant by being patient-driven. It is literally putting patients in the driver's seat and actively soliciting their input to help improve every touchpoint on the patient experience. It's especially important as organizations work to redo or revamp aspects of the patient experience or attempt to resolve a problem that has caused complaints. Instead of assuming or guessing what patients want (which is a patient-first or a patient-centered approach...still good but not patient-driven), organizations that are patient-driven rely on patients to share what their personal experience has been like and what specifically could be done to improve. The organization (and specifically the organization's culture) must be internally designed to deliver the desired experience of its patients.

The key is to continue to meet patient needs on the clinical side and to exceed patient expectations on the service side. We do this by actively engaging patients and their families in the delivery of care. But it's not a one-time thing.

Organizations that are patient-driven (or customer-driven) know that it is a built-in continuous improvement process. In order to be crystal clear on what patients want, organizations must check in regularly with patients to ensure the removal of any and all pain points of navigating the patient experience. That is the key to being more than just patient-first or patient-centered; that is the key to being patient-driven.

93

Develop Your Culture - Don't Just Teach to the Test

One of the greatest moments in my Disney career is when I was selected to teach Walt Disney World's New Employee Orientation, or what we simply called, *Traditions*. Nine of us were selected that year, out of a pool of many cast member applicants, so I felt very honored to be chosen. Seven of the nine of us were hourly, frontline employees, and two were frontline managers. The audition was a multistep process over three weeks. And the formal training program was five intense days that enabled us teach an eight hour interactive workshop and property tour, once or twice a month, for one year. And every year, Disney would repeat this process and bring in a new group of Traditions instructors.

So you may be asking yourself, why would Disney choose to use front line employees to teach their new employee orientation program instead of using their professional human resource managers or a cadre of subject matter experts (as healthcare typically does)? My simple response to you is, culture.

After all, a company's culture is its basic personality, or what employees might refer to as "the way we do things around here." Culture is the system of values and beliefs an organization holds that drives their daily actions, habits and behaviors. And when those daily habits are positive and intentional, it can align and energize the workforce, drive teamwork, and move the organizational mission and customer service forward. But when that culture is implicit, undefined, and left to grow on its own, it can suck the life out of the workforce and unintentionally create a workforce of minimalists, kill productivity, and make the organizational mission, vision and values nothing but a punchline for employee jokes. And as for customer service, well, then you roll the dice. Sometimes you get random acts of kindness, and other times you get an employee with an attitude of indifference. The only real consistency seems to be in the inconsistency.

So again, why does Disney use front line employees to train its cast of thousands? Who better to teach the intentional culture of what the organization stands for and what it will not stand for, than those who are expected to live it each day? Every organization has their role model employees, who are authentic, believable and able to share the organization's story in their own words. It helps pass the all important new employee "snicker-test."

Over the years, I have found that when you build a warm, authentic, explicit culture, the customer satisfaction scores tend to follow in its tracks. Every leader in the world of business knows that employee engagement ultimately drives customer satisfaction, long term. But in healthcare today, I see a lot of hospital leaders chasing monthly patient satisfaction scores and not investing time actually developing their organization into an intentional culture.

We all know that your culture will eat your strategy for lunch! But if you and your employees can help make an explicit culture, one that is authentic and relevant to the work they do every day, it can not only align with your business strategy - but can be the catalyst for propelling you from a mediocre company to achieving world-class status.

Many say the definition of insanity is doing the same thing over and over again and expecting different results. In healthcare, isn't that exactly what many are doing? We purchase off-the-shelf training programs or scripts, conduct events and initiatives in the fervent hope that something will improve our low patient satisfaction scores. And when scores go up, we say, "Congratulations - you hit the 97th percentile this month! What did you do to achieve that?" And they answer: "Well, we tried a bunch of things…but we are not 100% sure." The next month, we ask, "Oh no! You dropped to the 15th percentile as compared to hospitals our size in our satisfaction database, what happened this month?" And they answer: "Umm, we're not sure."

With such inconsistencies and pressure to get our scores up, we are left with little choice but to purchase yet *another* new mandatory protocol, program or initiative to help. Many seasoned employees then say to their colleagues, "Here we go again! But don't worry…If we just lay down long enough, this program too will pass…just like all the other programs!" And unfortunately, they are right!

It's a common situation. A simple internet search reveals hundreds of articles with "solutions" on how to improve patient experiences. If you are looking to temporarily boost your patient satisfaction scores, these solutions may provide the perfect short-term fix; however, if you're looking for sustainable positive change, you can no longer just "teach to the test" and "strive for fives." You cannot change the patient experience overnight. These tactics must first have a vital prerequisite: **You must first change your culture.**

Changing your culture – or, at the very least, clearly defining it and aligning it with your strategic plan – takes time and effort, but the payoffs are worth it, both financially and intrinsically.

Changing the Organizational Dynamic

Successfully uniting culture and strategy involves thinking differently. We can no longer be just prescriptive. We cannot just launch another one size fits all laundry list of things employees should do or say to improve the patient experience.

Change happens when a patient-driven culture is woven into the DNA of your organization. **"This cannot become an additional thing we do, it has to become who we are as an organization!"** Joseph Jasser, MD, MBA, former CEO Dignity Health Medical Foundation

There are two keys to success in hardwiring a patient-driven culture.

1. **Involve departmental stakeholders in the process of building or redesigning the culture.**

Building a world-class culture is a lot like the program created by Habitat for Humanity, where volunteers of the community come together to build a home for a family who cannot afford one on their own. Many of these volunteers have never built anything by hand before. Most have never used a circular saw, a power drill or a nail gun. But my company is like construction engineering. We have the skills, the expertise and the tools to help them build a world-class culture or 'house of excellence' that is uniquely theirs. We just need them to show up and help bring these blueprints to life.

For any culture change to be successful and lasting, it must grow organically, ideally through a true grassroots effort. It must be created and embraced by providers, staff, and leaders working together as architects in its design. Culture change cannot be perceived as just another top-down initiative, or flavor-of-the-year effort. Those quick-fix programs are a lot like laying down AstroTurf, it looks good at first, but because it isn't tied to who

you are, it never really takes root and grows naturally. Culture is like natural grass: it needs soil, rain, and sun…but you need to cut it and weed it now and again or that grass will go to pot.

The key to designing your authentic culture is that it is must designed by you and your patients, for you and your patients. Gather employee representatives from all major areas of the patient experience to be the architects of your cultural blueprints. These employee architects should be both clinical and nonclinical, executive and frontline, and patients. In the end, we must be able to say, "This was developed by us and our patients, for us and our patients."

> **"This was designed <u>by</u> us and our patients,**
> **<u>for</u> us and our patients."**

2. Develop a common set of tools, common language and clear end goals.

Everyone must be able to clearly define what it is they stand for (see lesson to "Develop Your Organizational True North"), and the behaviors they will no longer tolerate. Clarity creates alignment; a common language and tools create empowerment; and a consistent decision-making process creates consistency and mutual accountability throughout each step of the patient experience.

The ILS transformation approach is very authentic, yet comprehensive and must first start with:

Involvement: to select and guide your multidisciplinary team of formal and informal leaders to participate in the cultural assessment and then be the architects in the design of the new explicit culture. This generates a sincere and authentic culture which the authors…

(Authorship) take great pride and **Ownership** in. These owners now want to make sure everyone has…

Mutual Accountability to live day to day and will desire to make sure the proper infrastructure is built for **Sustainability**.

WHEN YOU INVOLVE EVERYONE IN THE DESIGN
OF THE NEW CULTURE.
THEN THIS LEVEL OF AUTHORSHIP LEADS TO OWNERSHIP.
WHEN THEY OWN IT, THEY WILL PROTECT IT, EVEN
WHEN YOU, THEIR LEADER, IS NOT AROUND.

- JAKE POORE

94

Are You Just Another Healthcare Provider? (The 4 Ps)

Can you do for healthcare what Disney has done for entertainment? What Ritz-Carlton has done for hotels? What Southwest Airlines has done for the airline industry? What Starbucks has done for the lonely coffee bean? How can you move from just another commodity to a must have destination of choice? What is your differentiator?

For decades, Michigan, New York and New Jersey were always top states when it comes to numbers of visitors coming to Walt Disney World in Florida. Along the way, how many Disney competitors did these visitors pass on their two-day drive to Orlando? How many hotels, water parks, and theme parks does the family of four drive right by until they finally arrive at Walt Disney World?

Walt Disney World Resort has become the number one single site vacation destination on the planet earth - more people visit there each year than any other single place. How did they do that?

Walt Disney World in Orlando and Disneyland in California are both destinations of choice because they offer what the customer wants - the unique Disney Experience. The Disney Experience can be described by the integration of the 4 P's: Product, Process, Physical Environment, and People.

PRODUCT: You must have a good quality product (attractions, food, hotels, rides) to become a destination that people will want to visit. Over time, if you don't have a good product, then people are not going to want to come.

PROCESS: Getting access to that product must be easy and accommodating (website, call center, tickets, reservations).

PHYSICAL ENVIRONMENT: Upon arrival, your first impression typically involves the physical environment. This includes landscaping, building facades, lobbies, uniforms, music, clean restrooms, a feeling of safety, etc.

Last but not least, **PEOPLE**: Your workforce must be incredibly professional, friendly, engaging, and proactive in seeking out guest contact.

Here's how we can apply these four P's to healthcare:

Healthcare does a great job of delivering the **PRODUCT**. We have the newest MRI machine, the best cancer center, or a state-of-the-art birthing suite. The clinical product regularly meets the highest standard. Clinical excellence will get patients in the door, but what gets them to **come back** is a combination of all four P's.

PROCESS includes access from admission to discharge. Everyone must own the process. For instance, whether you work in the emergency room, inpatient environment, outpatient, or primary care, is there a consistent process of entering a patient's room? Do you knock on the door or not? What's the process for greeting a patient in a waiting room? Does the medical assistant walk out to the waiting area and announce to the whole room someone's name? The last step is the discharge process. Patient belonging bags are rarely in the forethought of the patient experience. We find this is a missed opportunity to meet and exceed patient expectations and build some positive branding.

PHYSICAL ENVIRONMENT is huge. It starts with proper signage from the interstate to your campus and continues to your parking lot with labeled sections and parking spaces. Which entrance is the main entrance? When you walk in, do you know who's who by the uniforms they wear? Are the name tags legible and worn over the heart? Are the lobby restrooms clean? Are there handmade, paper signs anywhere? Are hallways named like streets in a city and themed or colored to make way-finding easier? Is there a positive decor and background music? We have to remember that everything in the patient experience either adds to the patient experience or distracts from it.

The one P that patients remember the most is their interactions with **PEOPLE** - clinical or non-clinical, front of the house or back of the house. What people say and what their body language communicates matters. The very best employees are a combination of the right attitude and aptitude.

In healthcare, we have to be masters of the entire patient experience, not just the procedure

95

Sometimes is the Enemy of Always

Jim Collins, author of the famous business book, *Good to Great*, says "good is the enemy of great" when defining the difference between good organizations and ones that become great. His point is that good organizations many times settle for being just good and never really seek to reach for that last extra inch to be great. Great organizations never seem to settle for being good. They build continuous improvement processes that force them to always to strive for excellence.

If "good is the enemy of great" in business, I would argue that "sometimes is the enemy of always" in healthcare. Why? Because patient satisfaction surveys are scaled and rated in a way that doesn't credit the delivery of positive patient experiences "sometimes." You only get credit for creating positive experiences ***always***.

Consider this:

• Some primary care physicians actively listen to their patients describe their symptoms and complaints. Others interrupt after 20 seconds to "help move this conversation along."

• Some nurses offer to close patient room doors so their room stays quiet and they can get a good night's sleep - others don't.

- Some food service workers offer to help elderly patients open milk cartons and sealed plasticware packaging. Others just drop food trays on the bedside table and run.

The bottom line is that when patients think we do things "sometimes," we receive a patient satisfaction score of between 0 to 8 (out of 10), but we actually receive a credit of 0. The only time we receive a positive rating at all is when the patient gives a rating of 9 or 10. Then we know we have created a consistent patient experience of *always.*

Creating a Culture of Always

The key to creating a culture of "always" versus a culture of "sometimes" is to engage the entire organization in the process of building something so specific and explicit, team members know it when they see it and they know when they do not. Eliminating cultural departmental silos is not enough. The culture has to work horizontally, across all departments, mirroring your patients' experiences with your organization.

Engaging everyone as an architect of the organizational culture is the difference between short-term compliance and long-term commitment. "If you build it, they will come" is a great movie line, but a more accurate mantra for a successful cultural transformation is: *If they help build it, they will own it.*

Ownership in the culture they create leads to strong feelings of pride, which lead to your staff protecting and policing the culture. That is when a grassroots culture catches fire.

Building a patient-driven, employee-owned culture is not enough, though. It has to be sustained. This requires engaged employees who are committed to delivering that "always" experience they helped define.

For current employees, a process must be in place to ensure that the message "This is how we do things here" is communicated horizontally and vertically to every corner of the organization and to every level of the care team.

96

Common Sense to Common Practice

In your organization, think about what specifically has become so imprinted in your culture, in your daily operation, in your interactions with customers (and each other), and even your physical environment, that "it" defines your standard of common practice in delivering healthcare?

Whose point of view defines "it"?

Our common sense and intuition easily resonate with a patient-driven model for care, but there is often a huge gap between what leaders are thinking or feeling and what they are actually doing.

The essence of Patient-Driven Care is being able to successfully cross the divide between Common Sense and Common Practice where every patient touchpoint with your organization reinforces your brand as designed around the human at the center of care.

In my years working at Disney, this was perhaps the number one rule that was reinforced for me and the thousands of cast members (employees).

Exceeding expectations – or creating "magic moments" for guests – was not only our service philosophy; it was our core business. And at the heart of this philosophy was the belief that no matter what your individual job task was, it was the attitude and demeanor of every single Disney employee that would either positively or negatively impact their entire experience.

And you know what? It's no different for healthcare.

How your patients and their families perceive your employees' willingness to go the extra mile and treat them as they wish to be treated is powerful. It influences their overall opinion of your entire healthcare organization.

So what are some things you and your staff can do right now to exceed patient expectations?

1. **Knock before entering a patient's room.**

2. **Introduce yourself.**

3. **Explain what you're doing (before, during, and after while avoiding medical jargon).**

4. **Make eye contact rather focusing on an electronic medical record.**

5. **Actively listen.**

6. **Ask patients what name they prefer you use ... and then use it.**

That last example is one of my biggest pet peeves and the main reason I shared the story about my father.

These are things that are not just nice to do. In the eyes of patients, they are priceless. And by incorporating them (and others) as part of your Common Practice, you can begin to create peace of mind for patients, build trust between caregivers and patients, and move closer to the goal of providing patient-driven care.

Working with organizations all over the country, I find that common sense is not always common practice. One great example is that while so many health care organizations claim that their top priority is to create great customer service, they base the lion's share of their physicians pay on Relative Value Units (RVUs.)

Imagine how a doctor must feel to be told that they need to take time, be kind, not rush… but then not be able to take a vacation because they will lose productivity points. Rather than a paid vacation, they are actually paying to take a vacation in some organizations.

It is not an easy problem to solve. Health care is business. Productivity matters. But we can't promise to put the human side of healthcare first on our billboards and then push only the business side in the board room. When the promises we make to our customers don't match our priorities, there is a disconnect that patients and families can feel.

The solution is to identify your priorities, communicate them to everyone, and reward the team for living up to them.

97

Create a Culture of Always

Most people find comfort in predictability because we are creatures of habit. Once we have a good experience with a company, we like to return to that same company. Whether it's a dry cleaner, supermarket, or restaurant, predictability brings peace of mind in an often chaotic day.

When my family and I travel across the United States, we know, with certainty, we can go to any McDonald's restaurant and get a predictable product and experience. Whether you like McDonald's food or not, you can't deny their level of consistency and predictability. There is consistency with their parking lot design, drive-thru, employee uniforms, name tags, restaurant layout, and restroom cleanliness. A Big Mac in Boston tastes just like a Big Mac in Seattle, and McDonald's has successfully replicated that blueprint world-wide (with nuanced adaptations to the local culture, tastes and language).

When traveling abroad and not speaking the local language, it can be stressful just finding directions and knowing how to order food. After many days on the road, many weary travelers can find comfort in occasionally going to a place where they know what they're going to get. You know what you are going to get at McDonald's, whether you can read the foreign language menu or not. Likewise, unpredictability can create uncertainty. And uncertainty can be unsettling.

Walt Disney understood this concept of predictability and the ability to replicate, which is one of the reasons he initially went into the film and movie business and not live show entertainment. After he and his team of animators spent years working on a single animated film, he knew with certainty that his product could be shown in movie theaters around the world with consistency. All theater owners were required to do was start running the film.

However, Walt sought to bring a higher level of experience to people. Rather than just watching a two-dimensional film on the silver screen, he wanted to turn the storytelling of films inside out and have the audience take part in the show, becoming immersed in the total experience. This is why he created Disneyland in 1955.

His challenge? Creating that same level of consistency and predictability in a theme park as he did in films with a young bunch of employees in the 1950's?

His solution? He used the concept of a show script. A show script is a story written out in great detail that includes the physical setting, cast wardrobe, and the speaking lines the cast are required to say to create a consistent, predictable show each and every time. And when "right fit" auditions are held, training is conducted, shows launched, and quality control monitored, a world-class, consistent product is born.

Again, there are many differences between Disneyland and healthcare. People plan ahead, save their money, and look forward to going to Disney. And the Disney experience is almost always positive. However, most people do not plan ahead, save their money, and look forward to going to a hospital. The healthcare experience can be a painful or a frightening experience. But does it always have to be this way? Can we minimize the negative aspects rather than contribute to them? What can we learn from the science of Disney and apply to healthcare?

Just like McDonald's, the Disney product is predictable. Each time you visit a Disney theme park, the experience is predictable, time after time, year after year. Predictability is the result of a culture of always. When we create a culture of always in a healthcare setting, we have the opportunity to take the fear of the unknown out of healthcare.

98

Don't Sacrifice Culture for Talent

If you apply for a job at the Walt Disney World Resort, you're really being *cast* for a **role in a show** - even if you're not a singer, dancer, or actor. Why? Because Disney doesn't just hire people to fill job positions. Every cast member must be a good fit for the position. And no matter how skilled the employee is, if they don't fit in with the culture of the Disney organization, and if they aren't reflecting Disney's service promise of *We Create Happiness* every day, they won't last long.

Have you heard the popular adage - culture eats strategy for lunch? At its core, it means that whatever strategy, initiative or program you put forth, it will only succeed if there is an explicit culture in place to support it.

So what happens if you *think* you have a strong, patient-driven culture and yet there are a few employees who do their own thing and don't quite buy in to the way things are done at your organization?

Now, imagine these employees are your top surgeon, your most skilled nurse, or your most talented accountant. Are you willing to replace your star employees if they're sabotaging your culture? If the answer is no, how will that affect your culture going forward?

99

Develop Your Organizational True North

Undoubtedly, the most powerful tool in your Disney Lessons arsenal is the ability to align and focus 74,000 employees toward the same end in mind. Disney calls it their "Service Theme." We call it your "Organizational True North," because a guiding compass only works if it points north, always. Stop any Disney employee, no matter what their job title is in the organization, and ask them to share their service theme. They will respond, *We create happiness.* Three words that are a memorable and powerful way to align an organization to the same end in mind.

Remember, a service theme is not your mission, vision or values (MVV). It's your MVV in work clothes. It's *the sum of all of our parts* that we're trying to instill in the minds of those we serve and to each other. And the most important word in that true north is *"WE"*. It does not matter where you work, or what you do…your role matters!

So what is your True North?

At Dignity Health Medical Foundation, it is also a short, memorable, internal phrase that unites every care team member towards to the same end in mind. And it is uniquely theirs; *designed by us and our patients, for us and our patients.*

"WE UNITE HEALING AND HUMANKINDNESS"

TO CREATE PEACE OF MIND FOR EVERY PERSON, EVERY TIME, THROUGH A CULTURE OF YES.

About the Author

Jake Poore is a former Disney leader, sought-after international speaker, and a leading authority on transforming the patient experience while building customer loyalty. He is on a mission to change the face of healthcare by uniting healing and human kindness.

Unlike typical trainers or keynote speakers, Jake spends most of his time in the trenches of healthcare, working side by side with clinical and non-clinical care team members on every step of the patient experience. You may find him shadowing a nurse on a medical-surgical floor, observing pre-op surgery, secret shopping the waiting room of a doctor's office or conducting patient focus groups.

As Founder and President of ILS, Jake knows what it takes to create and maintain a world-class service organization. He should...he spent nearly two decades at the Walt Disney World Company in Florida helping to recruit, hire, train and align their then 65,000 employees toward one end in mind: creating memorable experiences for individuals, not transactions for the masses. His career at Disney started in 1982 as a balloon seller on Main Street U.S.A. as part of the Disney College Program. He worked in many different jobs at Walt Disney World over the ensuing years.

In 1996, Jake helped launch the Disney Institute, the external training arm of Disney that sold its business secrets to the world. 80 percent of the people who attended the Institute were from healthcare...and Jake's passion for helping to improve healthcare grew.

Just after September 11, 2001, Jake launched Integrated Loyalty Systems, a company on a mission to help elevate the human side of healthcare. Since then, Jake and his team of experts have been sharing the organizational blueprints needed to build world class patient experiences by helping healthcare organizations design and execute patient-driven cultural blueprints, define their patient experience strategies, and map out and operationalize the ideal patient and employee experience.

Team ILS has successfully helped many healthcare organizations achieve cultural transformations including: Kaiser Permanente, Cigna Medical Group, Augusta Health, Dignity Health and their 75 medical practices, Baystate Health, Penn Medicine, Ochsner Health System, Sheltering Arms, National Rehabilitation Hospital, WMC Health and BJC Healthcare's ProgressWest Hospital.

Jake is an ACHE faculty member and teaches a 2-day course — sharing the blueprints for designing exceptional patient experiences.

In his free-time, he enjoys sailing, golf, and photography. He lives in Orlando with his wife and their three beautiful children.

About Integrated Loyalty Systems

Since 2002, Integrated Loyalty Systems (ILS) has focused its passion and efforts at the forefront of patient experiences in healthcare. With roots in some of the great "experience" companies like Disney, Starbucks and Southwest Airlines, the consultants and trainers at ILS work with clients to transform an organization's culture in a way that unites clinical quality and quality patient experiences. Always. Consistently.

With today's focus on "value" and reimbursements tied to survey results, ILS understands that short-lived, quick-fix, off-the-shelf solutions can actually do more harm than good for healthcare organizations that want to improve. The ILS Approach is one that serves as a catalyst for real, organic organizational change — created *by* patients and staff, *for* patients and staff — in ways that ensures everyone knows and supports the improved culture: "the way we do things here."

Listening to patients... involving staff... engaging clinicians... holding leaders accountable... all are part of a proven formula that is both art and science. Like the sculptor Michelangelo releasing David from the marble, ILS helps clients chip away at the barriers that have built up over time to allow clients to reconnect with and execute on the reasons they went into healthcare in the first place.

All of the patient experience improvement is wasted if the clinical outcome falls short, and ILS never loses sight of the fact that patients come to have their medical issues addressed. All of the smiles won't help a clinical interaction that falls short; however, when clinical pathways are delivered with patient-driven care and compassion, we know that the whole is greater than the sum of the parts.

Whether a short speech, day-long workshop, or multi-year consulting engagement, Team ILS brings a perspective unmatched in healthcare consulting: the ability to assess experiences through the patient's eyes (and ears, and nose....) and an array of specific tools that have proven to have positive impact on those. But tools are useless, unless there's a blueprint... which is why ILS works with leaders to install and hardwire a cultural blueprint to ensure delivering consistently excellent patient experiences is not just something our clients do — *it's who they are.*

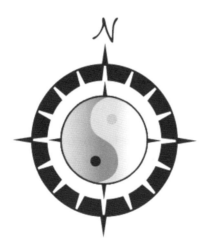

Helping to Deliver Patient Experiences that Unite Healing and Compassionate Care...*Always*

Integrated Loyalty Systems
Elevating the Human Side of Healthcare

HAVE YOU EVER BEEN IN AN ORGANIZATION THAT WAS DOING ONE OF THOSE 'PROGRAMS OF THE MONTH'?

You knew that after a while, the novelty and enthusiasm would wear off, and things would go back to normal. At Integrated Loyalty Systems (ILS), we take a different approach. At ILS, we work hard to ensure that everything we recommend reflects **your** unique organizational culture — not ours. Our approach doesn't impose a predetermined, prescriptive course, but instead reflects a carefully tailored solution that considers your existing service culture, leadership style and resources available.

Think of us as the architects of patient experience.

Our team leads hospitals and organizations through the comprehensive design of their unique cultural blueprints. We want to make a lasting and profound difference at your organization. We'll help you put systems in place, teach you how to integrate them together, and set you up for success and lasting loyalty, so your organization will continue to thrive long after we've left the building.

KEYNOTES ★ CULTURAL TRANSFORMATIONS
★ CUSTOMER SERVICE TRAINING ★
LEADERSHIP DEVELOPMENT ★ WORKSHOPS

Stay Connected

With Jake Poore and Integrated Loyalty Systems

Contact Integrated Loyalty Systems at:

PHONE	(407) 859-2826
EMAIL	info@WeCreateLoyalty.com
WEB	www.WeCreateLoyalty.com
FACEBOOK	Integrated Loyalty Systems
TWITTER	@jakepoore. @wecreateloyalty
YOUTUBE	Integrated Loyalty Systems (channel)

Subscribe To Our Free E-Newsletter

The ILS e-newsletter, PX Solutions, is cherished by readers around the world and widely considered one of the most valuable newsletters available. It's an essential read for anyone looking to improve patient experiences. Once you subscribe, you'll find Patient Experience insights and solutions with a strong focus on things you can do today, regardless of what level in the organization you are. Even more important, the insights you'll discover in every free issue REALLY WORK. Subscribe today at info@WeCreateLoyalty.com

Resources

[1] ORead: KU Employee Newsletter. *KU study shows doctors who sit during visits perceived better by patients.* April 19, 2010. http://oread.ku.edu/~oread/2010/april/19/stories/sit.shtml

[2] Swayden, Kelli J., Karen K. Anderson, Lynne M. Connelly, Jennifer S. Moran, Joan K. McMahon, Paul M. Arnold. Effect of sitting vs. standing on perception of provider time at bedside: A pilot study. *Patient Education and Counseling.* Volume 86, Issue 2, February 2012, Pages 166-171. https://www.sciencedirect.com/science/article/pii/S0738399111003053

[3] University of Pittsburgh, Changing Experiences Through Empathy - The Adventure Series, https://thisisdesignthinking.net/2014/12/changing-experiences-through-empathy-ge-healthcares-adventure-series/

List of Photos and Attributions

Page x: Eddie Poore. Source: Jake Poore

Page xi: Jake selling balloons. Source: Jake Poore

SECTION HEADER: Head, Heart, Hands graphic. Source: ILS

Page 4: Patient Experience graphic. Source: ILS

Page 13: Photo of Jake name tag. Source: Jake Poore

Page 18: Photo of towel animals. Source: Frieda Rivera

Page 41: Photo of button. Source: Jake Poore

Page 48: Photo of Epcot Entrance. Source: Kim Smith

SECTION HEADER - LEADERSHIP. Source: Shutterstock

SECTION HEADER - EMPLOYEE BEST PRACTICES. Source: Shutterstock

SECTION HEADER - UNDERSTAND THE PATIENT PERSPECTIVE THROUGH THE "PATIENT'S EYES". Source: Shutterstock

Page 100: Photo of smiley face bandage. Source: Jake Poore

Page 108: Photo of Happy Birthday button. Source: Jenna Kinkade

Page 113: Photo of security guard shack. Source: Jenna Kinkade

SECTION HEADER - SERVICE BEHAVIORS. Source: Jonathan Pennell- Shutterstock

SECTION HEADER - CREATE A CARING LANGUAGE. Source: Shutterstock

SECTION HEADER - HUMAN KINDNESS AT WORK. Source: Shutterstock

Page 158: Photo of Baby Care sign. Source: Jenna Kinkade

SECTION HEADER - EVERYTHING SPEAKS. Source Shutterstock

Page 171: Photo of Holding Hands. Source: Shutterstock

Page 176: Photo of Disney Welcome Sign. Source: Pixabay public domain

Page 193: Photo of Vic. Source: Jake Poore

Page 211: Photo of Patient Belonging Bag. Source: Jake Poore

SECTION HEADER - CULTURE. Source: Shutterstock

Page 233: Photo of Astroturf. Source: Jake Poore

Page 238: Photo of Partners Statue. Source: Frieda Rivera